MW00653601

Front cover by Mark Williams
Copyright 2014 by John Krache
Registration Number TXUI-910-309

BIO

John Juan is the recipient of no awards, yet. He lives with his wife on the Kitsap Peninsula of Western Washington and has five children and four grandchildren. However, he has a story to tell. His lead character, Joe, has had high adventure since he was a little boy. The adventures, whether it be hiking three active volcanoes; Saint Helens in the USA, Mt Aerinol in Costa Rica, or Api in the Banda Islands of Indonesia, or even Yellowstone Park are his hot adventures. During his climb to the top of the crater at Api, his shoes got so hot he had to descend. There was a long cooled off lava flow on one side that covered the land all the way into the sea. The next day he was able to scuba dive on the beautiful underwater lave flow.

Indonesia, Hawaii, Micronesia, Thailand, the Great Barrier Reef, the Caribbean Sea, Red Sea and Puget Sound are his wet adventures. Sharks, tuna, pelagic fish of all types cruise by like on parade on Joe and Ned's dives at the Blue Wall in Micronesia. The current from the deep that comes over the wall was so strong they hooked a cord to the reef to keep themselves stable near this remote island in Micronesia.

Whistler/Blackcomb, the mountains of Utah, Colorado, Idaho, Oregon, and Washington as well as Alaska are his cold Winter adventures. Joe and his buddies were able to visit five destinations in six days during a ski trip to Utah. Small avalanches, chutes, trees, jumps, tree holes all came into play on this great adventure. These adventures as well as rock festivals, concerts, and other music events are described within in detail. If you are an "adventure junkie" like Joe, these books are for you!

Revues

Anyone who writes a book deserves more than $10 for this book. I really liked your colorful language – keep it up. Uncle rod

John – good to hear from you and I think your book is great Bob D.

Thank you so much for your good book. I am about half way through and am really enjoying it. Keith P.

So much adventure in this book, and in so many places Corky P.

I'm about half way through your great book so far. It's taking me a while to read because I have no power in this cabin, so I read during the day. John S.

I liked your book so much I passed it on after I read it to my uncle who in turn passed it on to his son. I'm looking for more. Shane.

This book clearly reflects the way it was during our hippie times. It was a pleasure to read it. Ed W.

John I really enjoyed your book and my wife even liked it. Dur B.

Colorful cover to cover. John G.

Your main character Joe is such a hell??. I've really enjoyed this book. Criss F.

I think your book The Adventures of Mr. Zig Zag is very funny. I haven't laughed this much for a while Jimmy.

The Adventures of Mr. Zig Zag is very exciting to me since I lived those times. Allen W.

This book is very exciting to me in many different ways. I'm looking forward to sequal. Tim D.

My wife and I both read this book and were captivated and passed it onto my son. Bob and Jen M.

INTRODUCTION

This is the story of a boy inspired by adventure. It is a fiction based on fact. It chronicles his journey from childhood to manhood, and includes the characters he met along the way. This book was written in the hope that others will be inspired to seek adventures of their own, through all phases of life, and know that they have succeeded at living.

John Juan

TABLE OF CONTENTS

Table of contents continued

CHAPTER 1

IN THE BEGINNING

I was regaining consciousness, dazed and confused laying at the bottom of one of our living room walls. I had just been back handed by my burley step dad. He had my mom on her back beating the "crap" out of her, when I came up behind him and stabbed him in the back with a pair of scissors. I was doing what I could to stop the assault on my mom. My older brother Matt also tried to stop him and was punched so hard he had flown right through the plywood panel in the front door and was out "cold" on the front steps.

My mom, two brothers and I were living in a small nondescript house on Snyder Avenue in Bennington on a large peninsula in Puget Sound. My mom was single at the time having divorced our "blood father". My name is Joe. My two older brothers are Matt and Jan. Our mom was supporting us totally on her own and had two jobs. One as a waitress the other as a bartender at night. We had a good life, but didn't see my mom as much as we'd like. Our "hood" was near the salt water, and was full of kids.

My brother Matt was the oldest, about ten years older. He had jet black hair, handsome, and was already getting noticed by girls. He kinda assumed the dad role as the older usually does, and was very standup. He always stood up for me.

Mom and Me

My brother Jan, about nine years older than me, was more of a joker. He hung out at an Indian family's house nearby, and spent a lot of time with the son Rick Beaumont.

My mom had to work so much she wasn't around a lot, so my brothers and I ran amuck sometimes. My brothers were on the move, like they were both at one time or another Bennington yo-yo champs, marble champs and played some sports. Because we lived so close to the water they spent a lot of time fishing, and were sometimes successful at catching cod and ling cod. I was even sometimes successful at catching cod using clams, hooks of bent out safety pins and string over the next couple years. Imagine the joy we had when we could bring home a cod that was great eating. My brothers always had a little boat stashed in the bushes down in the cove. When they were out front in the cove I was confined to the beach. Because of my age and no life jacket I couldn't go on the pier. My brothers caught ling cod at times, and once they got one up to the boat and could see the head under the front of the boat and the tail at the other. This was a six foot plywood pram, so I could see it was a six or seven foot fish. They couldn't figure out how to get the big fish in the boat with no net, so my bro Matt stuck his hunting knife in the fishes head. The fish kicked and broke the line and down he swam with the hunting knife still stuck in his head. Too bad - that fish would have fed us dinner for at least a week. Years later as a scuba diver, I dove the cove and saw that the bottom was a series of tall clay ledges with undercut places for big cod to hide.

Jan always had lots of bicycles and I counted twelve at one time. He would take them apart and make all these weird grotesque bikes. His friend Rick borrowed one of these to go to the store to get family groceries. He was coming back down Cemetery Hill with a big bag of groceries in his arms and no hands on the handle bars. He was hauling and he hit a bump, lost control and got broken bones and road rash pretty bad. He looked like hamburger for a time.

When it was foul outside sometimes my brothers had Train's - not the mini type but the ones that were about the size of a loaf of cheese, and they could take the cab off the locomotives and all that was left was a fast motor with four wheels. They then set up jumps and crazy looking courses for them. They were masters at altering things for more excitement. We had an evergreen tree in our front yard that had very strong branches that were spaced on an even plain so that we could put a rug, cardboard or something on the branches to make a flat area, and yes we slept up there on occasion. I think my bros could make anything exciting.

We had good neighbors next door, Myna and Harvey, a very easy going couple who kinda kept an eye on us, but weren't too nosy. They had a boy and girl that I would know in my later life. Behind us was a family with a girl my age, a little younger boy in later years that was known as Homo. I didn't spend much time over there and only knew the dad was a cabby and the mom was stay at home. Two doors over were the Brewers - a couple of drunks. My mom had to rescue me from there numerous times. She made fudge with beer and sometimes I wandered over there and ate that fudge. My mom came to her door looking for me and Mrs. Brewer hid me in the closet. Of course my mom figured this out right away. She also got drunk and sat on the fence rails in their yard and hooted and hollered and rode like she thought she was on a horse. One day coming from the local store with my bros, we saw Mr. Brewer walking down a hill from the store. He had a gallon of wine in each of his arms and he started losing his balance and subsequently started staggering backwards. Of course he lost it, fell on the back of his head and busted it open. Then he dropped the wine which broke. My bros helped him up, he put his hand on his bleeding gash and stumbled home. These people drank so much that they had the entire garage filled with bottles. In those years beer bottles all had a deposit on them. They turned them in and got enough money to buy a car, which of course they were always too drunk to drive, so it sat in the garage where the beer bottles used to be.

Matt and Jan were always very good to me, but Jan could be tough. The street in front of our house was being dug up, and manholes for storm drainage put in. These were upside down bell shaped concrete structures with a manhole in top at street level. The workers would put them in place, then pour cement in the bottom about six or eight inches for the floor. I got too close, the cover was off and I fell in. It was about a six or seven foot drop, but because of the fresh cement, I didn't get hurt and stood in the cement and cried. My brother Jan heard me and came over to the hole and looked in. "What are you doing down there Joey"? In my tearful voice I said "I fell in and can't get out"! He promptly slid the cover on and walked away. It was dark in there, and I really started bawling. A few minutes later Jan and Matt came back and put a ladder down and rescued me. I think to this day I'm still traumatized -Ha Ha. On another occasion we were walking down to the theatre on Callow Ave. There was snow on the ground and my brothers were standing on the corner jumping out and grabbing car bumpers and skiing on their shoes until the driver either yelled at them or stopped. They finally got tired of this and we continued down the road. A big dog ran out from a residence and bit me. My bros jacked the owner up for $ 20.00 to cover the damages. It hurt like hell, but Matt consoled me and we continued to the theatre. All I got out of the bite was 50 cents fare into the movie and a 25 cent popcorn - they kept the rest.

I was out at the garage looking at Jan's bikes and for some reason I drank some ammonia. Fortunately Jan figured out what I did and went next door to Myna and Harvey's. They got me to puke and started feeding me evaporated milk, we were happy they were there and I got over it - no permanent damage. At that time my grandpa was still alive and walked to our house sometimes. He was well known in his working days for giving the gate guards liquor and taking wheel barrows of tools out of the Naval Yard after hours. He had fathered seven children, 5 girls and 2 boys. It was common to walk in their home and hear my uncle Rod, in his high teens by then, playing Boogie Woogie music on the piano. Most of my Grandparent's kids, except my mom, moved to California. My grandpa would stop by Safeway and look for good grub in the stores throw away. Sometimes he brought over veggies and fruit that was still good and we weren't proud so we washed it and ate it. One afternoon he came by our house, and he was so proud of himself. He had found what appeared to be an angel food cake with icing on it in the original box. Jan grabbed it and said it really felt light. He turned it over and it was an angel food cake pan that had frosting on it. I guess they had really fooled grandpa!

Down at the local High School, a twenty minute walk from our house, Gorgeous George was to wrestle on Sat. night. They had put a fight ring in the center of the gym right under a big skylight. Matt and Jan lifted me up and we all watched the bout through the skylight. We felt pretty good about watching a famous wrestler like Gorgeous George so close; but from up there we could really see how phony it was. He took a swing and missed the other guy by six inches, but the other guy would fall down and roll around. We got a good laugh out of the bout.

My bros sometimes flew kites for days. We got these great winds in February and March that lasted for days. They would get rolls and rolls of string, make a traditional rectangular kite, and use a big fishing pole and reel. Sometimes they stayed up all night and put their kite up for days. We could blow up a paper bag put a wire on it and put the ring on the kite line and it went all the way up the string to the kite. The kite could fly so high up it was hard to see. If they put to many paper sacks up there the weight brought down the kite. About this time Matt was old enough to drive. He got a job at a local bowling alley setting pins. There were no mechanical pinsetters, and it was all done by hand. The pin setter set the pins, and then jumped up on a ledge around the pins and hoped the pins wouldn't fly too hard and hit him. He was able after a while, with his old paper route money, and pin money to buy an old Plymouth. This car looked odd as it was a coupe with a really large trunk. He took the rear seat out and kinda boxed it in with an access door, and it made the trunk so big he had a bed in it. I'm sure some girls saw it firsthand. I loved this car as drive - in - movies were just getting going and because my bros had to watch me, I was able to go along with my brothers sometimes. The only movie I can recall

seeing was the Superman movie - no not with Christopher
Reeves but with George Reeves the original Superman.

About this time my mom met Tom. He was a burly
man, about 250 lbs. which looked a little odd as my mom was
120 lbs. wet. He really didn't have a real job, and picked brush
for a living. Brush consisted of huckleberry or salal and was
used for floral arrangements. Sometimes Tom, Matt, Jan, and I
all went. First time I went along he had an old Packard sedan
and my door flew open on a turn and I was suspended by the
door handle in space until Tom reached out and grabbed me. He
gave me a quarter for picking - big deal.

I got the feeling with Tom I was just necessary baggage,
and he didn't show me much attention one way or another. He
did take my mom and I to the Canal, a big salt water canal for a
day. Mainly he and my mom made out while I played floating
on big cedar rounds. These were three or four feet wide and a
foot thick and were really fun.

There was a growing concern about communism.   This
was the McCarthy trials. People of all walks of life were being
grilled by the government about whether they were communists
or not. I was in 1st grade at the time and my teacher Ms. Augusta
was a real grump but what was really a big deal was when we
saw her on TV being grilled by the government whether she was
a commy or not - and she admitted she was. She was replaced as
my teacher and I never saw her again -wonder what happened to
her?

One night my mom took me to the Carlo Club with her.
Wilt Chamberlain was making an appearance there, and his
whole gig as well as talk to patrons, was his heavy shoes which
made it possible to lean heavily each way. It was quite a sight

and I'll never forget standing in front of him astonished at how tall he was. At six years old I thought he looked like a giant in front of me.

One day we were all hanging around the house, which was great with Mom there, as it was usually just us boys. Matt had made one of his sandwiches with a half inch slab of onion with a thick layer of mayonnaise on each side. I don't know how he thought it was good, but when he ate it he got big dribbles of mayo down each side of his face.

Tom came in and started a big fight with Mom. Soon he had Mom down on the floor on top of her beating the crap out of her. I'd never seen Tom get like this with Mom, and I was crying, and wanting to protect Mom. I grabbed a pair of scissors and ran over and stabbed Tom in the back with them. It got his attention even though they sank in less than an inch. He back handed me so hard I hit the opposite wall. About that time Matt jumped him, Tom hit him so hard he flew through the center plywood panel in the front door, and ended up out cold on the front steps. Our neighbors Myna and Harvey saved the day when they came over and yelled at Tom, and being the coward he was he ran off. That was the end of Tom. My mom had a good friend cop, who came by and made sure Tom came by no more.

It was all a shame as Tom had started a delivery company. My mom was dispatching out of the house, and Tom and Matt were driving the delivery truck. I thought finally we were going to have a real business and be prosperous. But with Tom attacking my mom, we were just glad to have him gone and my mom safe. Matt had come too on the porch and we both recovered from being hit - no long term damage done. At that point my brothers nicknamed me "Guts", partly because I had a big disproportionate belly and had stabbed Tom with the scissors.

Mom went back to both previous jobs and life got back to normal.

My mom dated a couple of guys - one was a naval officer. He was ok but not very endearing as we could sense he was purely there for my mom.

We had snow sometimes, not much because we were so close to salt water. It seldom got cold enough to snow but when it did all the kids in the hood made full use of it. Haddon Hill was unique as it was fairly steep, long, and it turned a right turn onto another street, then went around in a less steep almost circle before it ran out. Then we could walk up a fairly short very steep hill and be right up to the top again. Kids went down the hill on sleds, plastic tarps, inner tubes, cookie sheets, scraps' of linoleum, toboggans, and anything that would go. What Fun! My mom and I were cuddling in her bed one morning when she told me, and my brothers she had met a really great guy at the Carlo Club. He was a trumpet player in a band that performed there. Soon we met the guy, Dewey, and we could tell right away he was good. I didn't know it then, but he would be the love of my mom's life, and the man I called Dad forever more. He told us all he wanted to marry my mom, and he loved us all. We were all so happy.

He did marry my mom and they sold the little house on Snyder, and we moved to a bigger rental house on Marguerite. This was a better place and had a good amount of land and a big orchard, including apple, cherry, pear and even a fig tree. The only drawback was that it was quite a ways from the salt water -

which I had really been drawn to. Salt water became an integral part of the rest of my life.

My mom had to kiss a lot of frogs, before she found her prince. Dewey grew up in Hoquium Washington on the coast. His dad was a logger until he had a tree he was topping hinge over on his knee and crush it. He had to wear a plastic sleeve over his knee as it evidently would not heal. At that point he bought a fishing boat and became a commercial fisherman. Dewey worked on his boat somewhat, but it really wasn't his calling. His mom tried to make a sissy out of him but didn't succeed. My dad started playing piano when he was quite young, but changed to the trumpet. Trumpet players were a lot like guitar players are today in bands. They played mostly lead, and Dewey really relished the spotlight. He told me he and his dad Otto had tough times making it around the depression and had to poach ducks at the ocean beaches nearby, and forage for cases of food that had fallen off cargo ships. I really liked Otto and was very sad when he died. He was a good man, and when we came over to visit, we always went down to the basement and worked on fishing gear and stuff. He always kept a pint of whiskey stashed in the rafters in the basement, and didn't want me to tell anyone about it, as he didn't want his wife to find it. His wife was kind of ritzy and wouldn't approve, though I think she knew any way.

My best friend at Marguerite was Chucky, a red head, chunky kid who also was a seeker of fun. We thought the granite chunks in his mom's garden were like gold, and we collected it and put it in an old strongbox we had, and buried it. Chucky's dad was always yelling at us about it. "Where are my rocks"? Our neighbor on the other side was Otto the cop. He was a Bennington police officer, and we were happy to have him there, because it wasn't the best neighborhood.

My brothers took BB guns apart and stretched the spring so they had more power. We could put a BB completely through a bird. We were always shooting at birds to keep them from eating the fruit.

There was a small store down on the corner and I did whatever I could to get money to buy candy. A candy bar was a whole nickel, and was about twice as big as they are now. I later knew the owners son, and took care of maintenance at his store. Chucky and I were becoming aware of girls, and at the right time of evening could see the neighbor woman through her window coming out of the shower naked. She was a beauty and I even think she saw us watching her and did nothing about it. Maybe she got hot like we did.

My dad decided he wanted a trumpet playing son, and since I was the youngest, I was selected. First he gave me just a mouthpiece. I tooted that thing constantly. Eventually trumpet was not my calling, but for now it was exciting. I wanted to make my new dad happy and did.

Matt was hanging with a girl and decided he wanted to marry her, and move out. That left just the four of us and about this time my dad changed my last name to his. He didn't change my bros as they were older - in their late teens by then. This was to be my third last name in my life. It was kind of confusing at school because I would see kids I knew earlier, and they called me by my old last name, and I had to correct them.

The Cleavers

Led Zeppelin

Life at Marguerite was somewhat uneventful compared to what was to follow, and Dad announced we were to move. He had bought a house and I had never even seen it yet. My mom declared it was exciting - and how right she was.

CHAPTER 2

THE POINT

My mom wasn't lying! We moved to a house on a point that stuck out in the salt water on Puget Sound. I'll never forget when I got out of the car and walked by the house to the top of the bank overlooking the salt water. I thought I died and went to heaven. I could see it was to be the most fun place to live by far! The house was a good looking medium sized 3 story home with a great view of the water.

Our neighbor on one side was a throwback sort of person; old ways; harsh sort that I liked anyway. He was eventually known as "The Viking" by me and my buddies because of his old ways. He had a huge train set in his basement. He built tunnels, hills, towns, even forests around his trains, and sometimes let me run them. He had old bear trap skis and when it snowed, we took off cross - country on the roads. Pretty soon I could hear him yodeling. I was real young and didn't realize how corny he was. A few times when it froze on the Eastside, he gave me ice skates and we went to a shallow pond to skate. I knew if I wanted to do something, he would help me. The Viking could also get mad at me. Once I chopped on a fir tree in his yard and he got so red faced mad, he looked like he was going to have the "big one"!

The neighbor on the other side "Mel", was also good to me. He gave me an old wooden boat; I put a mast and boom on it made from pecker - pole firs from his yard. Mom gave me an old sheet and I sailed all over the bays. This was my first boat, and I loved sailing in it.

We soon found we had steamer clams on our beach, and my friends and I could dig them; start a fire on the beach, boil the clams, and eat clams and sail all day.

We had some exciting places to go. One we called "disappearing Island" as when the tide was in it had 200 feet of 6 foot deep water around it. When the tide was out it had 200 feet of 2 foot deep mud surrounding it, so no one could get there without a boat at high tide. Dino, Dave, and I took our sleeping bags, clams and sailed down there and stayed on the island overnight. It was great to be on our own like that.

Fishing was good nearby, and we could go over to the NAD docks, get under the docks, knock barnacles off the pilings, and get piling worms for bait. There were many rock fish there, and we got good at catching them. My mom always made fish and chips and we along with other neighborhood kids scarfed them down.

My remaining brother at home, Jan, fished cutthroat trout and did well. He sometimes put a big wad of bacon on a hook and slung it out in the channel, and when a seagull bit it, he could play the seagull as it flew around trying to get off. Then he cut the line and let it go. I eventually started doing it too.

One spring a "Killer Whale" or Orca, wandered into the channel and into the bay. Jan wanted to try to catch it, so he got a barrel; big line; a hook, and put a chunk of roast beef on it, and anchored it in the middle of the channel. I don't think Orcas eat roast beef. Of course he never got a bite, I could hear shotguns going off all day in the bay. Those idiots were trying to kill the Orca, as back then they were hated because they eat salmon. Well they succeeded, the Orca was found on Alki Beach in Seattle dead of shotgun holes. It was really sad, and fortunately opinions changed about the Orcas. Soon after Orcas like "Namu" were being trapped in Puget Sound and sold to zoos. But I'll never forget Dave and I skipping stones on the beach, and that unfortunate Orca's fin popped out of the water 100 feet from us. It was a male which has a 3 to 4 foot fin. It was an awesome sight; we just wished he would have survived the ordeal in the bay, to reach maturity naturally, for this was the one that was blown to pieces.

During this time Elvis's Blue Suede Shoes and Jail House Rock along with Fats Domino's Blueberry Hill, Chuck Berry's Nadine; rock n roll music was being played on the radio. I was over at Dino's house hanging out, and he had a new record of Chuck Berry's called "One Dozen Berrys" and we couldn't believe how "cool" it was. At that point I started a lifelong love of rock music, and I've craved it ever since.

Rich and I noticed a pop machine outside of the Shore Motel up on the main drag that had the pop bottles in it on their side behind a glass door. We started thinking if we had a bottle opener and a big cup or something; we could hold the container under the bottle; open it, and fill it with pop. That's what we did, of course; they were all mixed together, but we gorged ourselves with pop. It only worked a couple of times then that machine was taken out. Good while it lasted. Rich and I were supposed to be camping out that night, but we continued from the pop machine to the drive-in-movie and snuck in. I don't know how

my dad found out but I got grounded for a while over it. I stood
on Rick's shoulders and put my middle finger out in front of the
projector that projected my middle finger on the big screen.

Dave had an aluminum boat, one of the first I'd ever
seen, with a 7 ½ horse Johnson outboard. We were small enough
that we could water ski behind it. We started off with double
skis but soon got to single skiing. We did that all day long
during summer. Of course we had our usual steamed clams on
the beach for lunch. When we needed gas we grabbed the can
and climbed all the way up this big 75 degree bank to the
Bingers Gas Station, at the top. Talk about a work out, but it was
necessary if we wanted to ski. None of us were old enough to
drive yet.

I wanted a fast boat and got some plans out of a Popular
Mechanics book called a "Punkin Seed". I was only twelve or
thirteen but thought I could do it. I was working for neighbors
off and on and had enough money to send for the templates, etc.
for the boat. It finally came, and I had enough money to buy
wood for the keel and ribs. I used my dad's tools, but he had
pretty crappy tools. My dad was working days in the local
shipyard and playing in his band on weekend nights, and didn't
have the time to work on wood projects or even help me. My
brother Jan was working as a carpenter at a furniture factory, so I
got a little bit of tools from him. I had no electric tools, so I had
to cut everything by hand in our basement where my boat was
being built. Eventually, without any help, I put the frame
together. I needed plywood for the skin, and made the mistake
of trying to take a couple of sheets out the back, after hours, of a
local lumber yard. I got busted red handed, but Izzy was good

enough, after I told him what I needed it for, to let me work it off. I got some of the skin screwed and glued to the frame but just couldn't quite get it all on and felt really beaten. I was really beaten and depressed. Jan came along and asked "why the long face Joey". I told him and being a good brother and carpenter he helped me finish the skin. I was pretty proud that I built a fast little boat at my age with only a little help. I needed a fast outboard motor, and my dad was so impressed - he took me up to Stewart, and bought me a fast 7 ½ horse Mercury racing motor. I conned some friends out of some steering and a crash throttle, paint and was ready. That boat was fast - it did 42 mph which was blazing speed for me. It was so fast I could get it to hop and run right over ducks trying to fly away ahead of me and catch up to any duck or seagull trying to outrun me. I got all the way to Blake Island in sight of Seattle in no time.

Most of us kids in the hood weren't old enough to drive, so we almost all had boats. We spent most of our time water skiing, racing, just tooling around in our boats during the summer months.

My dad had a runabout boat with a 45 Mercury on it. He decided one fine summer day himself, Mom, and I should go to Blake Island camping. Blake Island was kind of unique as it was in sight of Seattle and a lot of central Puget Sound. A man named Blake owned it, and built a big mansion on it. He had his own dock and private ferry that held a car or two that came on demand, and picked him or his wife up. Evidently his wife drove off the end of the pier and drowned. He was so grief stricken, he left the Island, mansion and all, never to return.

Over the years the mansion had been trashed and gutted. The island was given to the state eventually.

My mom was fond of going there because Blake had an orchard with loganberries. They had grown wild and crossed with wild black berries, and the result was these big tasty wild blackberries. That is why on this particular occasion we went to the island to pick berries. We anchored the boat and set up camp; explored the island for a while, then proceeded to pick big old pans of blackberries. My dad had stayed on the beach and was casting for our dinner. He caught about a 5 pound silver salmon and dinner was on. Mom added a few things from home to go with salmon and berries for dessert - what a great meal. That evening was calm and I got a good sleep. We were to leave the next day. The next day was blowing hard and got worse as the day went on. When Dad saw the big waves and whitecaps, he decided we should try the next day. We ate the last of our grub and crashed.

The next day was almost as bad, but Dad decided we should make a run for it. Turned out to be a good choice as we made it home safely after a lot of bouncing and taking on some water. When we came down off one big wave I put my bare foot right in a big pan of blackberries. Full pans of berries were all over the bottom of the boat. To that point, that was the roughest weather we had ever experienced on the water. The next day it was blowing pretty strong at home. Dino and I were both big Mad Magazine fans and had most all copies between us. We wanted to build a big Mad Magazine kite, and set about doing just that. After collecting the materials we built a 6 foot high traditional diamond shaped kite. We even drew a big bust of Alfred E. Newman on it along with Mad in big letters. We used a fishing reel with big line on it. The wind was blowing straight down the channel in front of the house. We went down on the beach and put it up. We had put about an eight foot tail on it to control it. We couldn't believe how powerful it was and took us both to hold it back. It kept ripping out line and was over houses at the end of the point. On one big gust it took a dive towards a house. It had wrapped the tail on a TV antennae, and on the next big gust it went straight up. It finally took all our line off the reel and last we saw of it, it crashed into the bay, antennae and all. Just another reason why the people on the point didn't like me much, and I had to work for Mr. Wilson to pay for his antennae.

Steve and I started buying firecrackers from Richard, the only guy in the neighborhood that sold them. All fun fireworks were illegal so they were hard to get. We could take 2 inchers, which the fuse burned underwater, and tape some weight on them. Then light them and drop them in the water, attempting to blow up crabs, and flounders on the bottom. I think we saw too many submarine war movies that showed them "depth charging". Anyway we graduated to bigger things, and I found out gunpowder was just charcoal, saltpeter, and sulfur, and we started making our own gunpowder and pipe bombs. A few of the neighbors lost mailboxes to us, and fortunately we lost interest before anyone got hurt. One more thing that didn't endear me to the neighbors.

Mom announced to our family she was pregnant. We were all so happy. Especially my step dad, who wanted a child of his own with my mom. I was so pumped about a possible little brother. Of course my mom after having three boys, was happy to have another shot at a girl. She would never get her girl.

Happy Day

CHAPTER 3

COONTZ

I was entering Junior High school - 7th and 8th grades.
The school was named Coontz, an ancient building in the middle of town. I was really excited about a new school; new friends, and a chance to play trumpet in the band.

My neighbor Mel, who took Steve and I roller skating tried to get us to join the Civil Air Patrol Cadets, but after visiting them, we weren't really interested. I did at the encouraging of a couple of older boys in the neighborhood, decide to join the Boy Scouts. It really was fun, at least at first, camping, boating, hiking etc. The scout master was sort of an idiot. He constantly told outlandish stories he couldn't back up. So we terrorized him as much as possible; like putting a bunch of salt in his food so it wasn't edible. Parker who was a big fat guy would arch up on his back and drop his ass, which shook the whole cabin when we slept in the loft. Our leader was always bitching at him about it. Sometimes we rolled up rabbit tobacco in toilet paper and smoked it. It would have probably been easier to just swipe some of my dad's Pall Malls. These smokes really tasted like crap, and I couldn't believe my dad smoked them.

We were staying in an old cabin in the woods when a freak storm dropped about two feet of snow, and we had to hike out the next day, because no one could drive in to get us. That was exciting stuff, as we thought we were saving ourselves. Steve and I decided we wanted to drive, so when my mom and dad went out in their boat, I took my dad's car keys and we'd go joy riding. Steve was already driving his family station wagon when he washed it. I didn't have a clue how to drive, especially a stick, so Steve started us out. My first time I almost crashed into a power pole. If Steve hadn't grabbed the wheel, it might have happened. One day my dad asked me why the steering wheel felt all sticky. I had to make up a story about just sitting in the car, and pretending driving. That was the end of taking the car. My dad was pretty wise, and I knew if I did it again he would bust me red-handed. We couldn't believe the neighbors never ratted us out because we were sure they saw us. Years later my mom told me dad had put a felt tip mark on the bottom of his tire that lined up with one on the garage floor. My dad thought I was taking his car but wouldn't confront me without proof. If we had taken the car again he would have had proof.

Steve kept driving in the form of washing the family wagon, and taking off in it afterward, much to his dad's displeasure. There were some comical skirmishes over there as his dad chased Steve around shouting for his car keys back. His dad was from the old country and could only speak clipped English. He called him Teevie, and his dad chased Steve down the road, up and over their carport, in one door and out the other of the house, and car. It was pretty comical and most of the neighborhood turned out to watch.

Dino and I figured out a couple of new ways to endear ourselves to our neighbors. We collected dog crap, and pooped and peed into a jar and bombed patios, sidewalks, and garages of our neighbors. Another prank was to break off the outside glass of a light bulb exposing the filament. Then we taped a firecracker to the filament, and stuck the fuse in the little curlydo wire part. Then Dino or I would sneak up to someone's porch

light and take their light bulb and replace it with ours. Then we
beat on the door and took off. When they came to the door at
night they turned on their porch light and stuck their head out the
door. About then the firecracker went off and scared the hell out
of them. We thought that was hilarious!

Another source of fun was road apple fights. Rick
Hagan, Dino, and I went down to Mr. Henry's place. He was a
nice old guy and had horses and a nice orchard - the only one left
in the neighborhood. When fall came and his apples were ripe,
he had the neighborhood kids over and we pressed apples and
took home a gallon each of apple cider. He was a war veteran
and at sundown he played taps on a bugle over the bay - unique
to our neighborhood! He didn't mind us having road-apple
fights in his orchard. He was such a good guy, we never pulled
any crap on him, nor would we allow any kids to.

Finally my mom had that child. It was another boy! I'm
sure my mom was a bit disappointed, but she never showed it.
My dad and I were ecstatic. My brothers were happy, but not as
excited as I. Matt of course was no longer at home and Jan was
in love with a girl, and was taking care of his own business. My
poor mom - no girls. My step dad had a daughter but we never
saw much of her. Now she lived with her mom, my step dad's
ex-wife and my previous step dad Tom. In effect my mom and
her traded husbands. We got the better end of that deal. Now I
had a little brother to be name Rory - but I always called him
"Chopper".

Coontz was my first try at sports. I could play at
some basketball, and decided to try out for the eighth grade team.
There were plenty of boys who were much better but I put up a
half-assed effort. When the cuts finally came I was the last one

to get cut. Since I didn't put out my best effort I wasn't terribly disappointed.

The rest of Coontz went along without much incident except I got kicked out of the band. What made it worse; I couldn't tell my dad, since I knew how important it was to him, to have a son that played trumpet as he did. Coontz had an open house and my mom and dad attended. The band teacher was an old friend of my dad's and he was so disappointed when Mr. Johnson told him I was kicked out of band. My dad didn't make a big deal out of it, but I could sense how disappointed he was. I finished up at Coontz and was getting excited about summer and going on to High School. Shortly after the headlines read "COONTZ BURNS TO THE GROUND"!

U. S. Swim Team

CHAPTER 4

HIGH SCHOOL

That summer was spectacular, as the weather was great, I had plenty of buddies, and plenty to do. We water skied most every day. We did again hike up the steep hill, through brambles and bushes with the 6 gallon gas tank to, and back down to get boat gas from Bingers. It was well worth the effort. Besides skiing and cooking our clams on the beach, we decided we could make our skiing more exciting by wearing old dresses. Occasionally the dresses got dropped and we skied around the bay naked. Oyster Bay was perfect for getting way out on the fringe while the boat was doing tight donuts - the result was going about 60 mph. A mistake at that speed meant rolling and tumbling across the water at break-neck speeds. Sometimes it hurt. I spent a few nights on Disappearing Island with my buddies and a few beers we were able to score. I found out Coontz had burned to the ground because some teenage fire-bug had torched it. To this day it is just a vacant lot turned into a soccer field - what a loss!

Rick and I spotted, inside of an open garage door, cases of beer. Since we were getting interested in spirits we decided to take some. We managed to take a few six packs here and there for a while, until we got the shits from some of it. About then we noticed the bottle caps looked different. I think we were taking home-made beer and the guy thought he would teach the beer thieves a lesson by bottling bad beer. But it gave me an

idea - why couldn't I make my own beer? I found a book that
laid it all out. A local store sold yeast, malt, barley and hops.
After finding a bottle capper in our basement, and scoring caps, I
set about making quarts of beer. After a few attempts I thought I
had it down. We put a couple of quarts in a small pack with an
opener, and went to the movies with my buds. We were up in
the balcony and we took my opener out and popped open the
quart. I had bottled it a little too soon and it shot everywhere.
After it settled down some we drank it and it wasn't bad. After a
while I got better at making it and kept bottling quarts. My
undoing came when some of the quarts I had stashed in the
rafters, got too warm and started blowing. My dad heard it but
didn't know what the explosions were. Finally the beer soaked
through the ceiling in my mom and dad's bedroom, and started
dripping on the bed. My dad made me stop and throw
everything away, but didn't severely punish me, because I think
he was intrigued by the fact that I was able to do it at my tender
age. Later we decided it was smarter and easier to get a swab to
buy it for us. American Bandstand was just starting and we
really liked the songs of Chuck Berry such as Nadine, Rock Roll
Music. Dino had Blueberry Hill, Runaway, and Tutty Fruity and
wore them out playing them. There was a new guy; a young
blind kid on American Bandstand - Stevie Wonder. I ended up
liking a lot of his songs over the years. Then rock started to
change some when we heard Spencer Davis Group. Steve
Winwood would make a lot of cool songs over the years. A few
neighborhood guys and I started taking our boats to NAD, an old
ammo depot about a mile away. It had closed a few years back,
and we took some wine we had scored, and set up a drinking
room in the top of one of the old buildings. I noticed everything

there was copper and brass - a discovery that would do me well later.

I started really noticing the girls and was getting next to some of them in the neighborhood. I was sneaking into one of the girl's room a couple houses over. It was pretty easy as her room was in the finished basement. Her gigantic boobs didn't escape me. Her name was Nadine, and she really was so-so on looks, but had a great body. Eventually I got busted, because her little sister spotted me, and ratted me out. I had to apologize to her folks, and was pretty embarrassed. Her mom didn't hold it against me. She was a God - fearing - woman who ended up being a good friend over later years.

I went down to the beach after school one day and saw Steve bullying some of the younger neighborhood kids on the beach. I wasn't going to allow this, and after some choice words threw him in the water. He had just bought new blue suede shoes. He stood up in the water and started crying and sniveling about his ruined shoes. The victimized boys just laughed at him, and he didn't try to bully them again. I felt pretty good and those kids thought I was a real hero. Even to this day we laugh about it.

Dad came up to me one day and said "you know I peed in the pint of whiskey, I keep in the rafters in the garage", and he hoped I enjoyed it. Evidently he thought I had been drinking his whiskey, but I didn't like whiskey and wouldn't have drank my dad's anyway. I knew right away Steve was the culprit, so I told Dad "I wasn't swiping it and was sure Steve was". My dad didn't like him much anyway, and we high-fived and had a good laugh over that one!

Right about this time I was losing interest in my boat, because a few of my friends were starting to drive their folk's cars. My dad knew better than to let me use his. I met a small guy who was always kinda laughing and funny. Pat had a car of his own - a 48 Ford coupe with a 6 cylinder in it. It felt pretty cool having a car to ride in. We did some drinking in it, and were able to go to parties - a new concept for me. The big time beer then, was Olympia - named for the city where it was made. The inside of the label had dots, and it was said if you found a "four dotter" you could give it to a girl and get some boinking for it. Of course that was a ridiculous fable - at least for us.

Pat barely had enough money to get gas for his car, and when we needed oil for it, it was a problem. His old man was fond of deep frying, and put the old oil in containers in the garage. We started using this oil in Pat's ride, and after a while it started smelling like fish-n-chips. It kept on running though and still got us around.

We started running around with a guy we just met named Ken Krill. He had his dad's big Ford station wagon to use and he just hammered it. We were surprised how long it lasted. At least twice when I was with him, he hammered it so hard the carburetor caught fire and we had to pour beer on it and put a towel on it to put it out. His dad finally got fed up and wouldn't let him use it anymore - by then it was pretty well trashed.

There was a story going around school about a girl named Jeannie who was putting-out to everyone. Evidently guys were going in her bedroom window. Eventually there was an article in the local paper about a popular kid at school who said

"He was at a keg party, when a farmer came on them and shot him in the ass". Well about a week later the real story came out. The kid was climbing in Jeannie's window and her dad shot him in the ass with rock salt. Regardless of the notoriety I'll bet he really hurt from it and thought it not worth the pain.

Thieving wasn't a big part of my life at that point, however I made a big mistake by getting caught stealing fishing gear out of Payless by a clerk who just happened to be a friend of my dad's. Dad was so mad, he made me go to Payless; return the fishing gear, and apologize to the clerk. When I got home my dad hauled off and back-handed me into the wall. He was pretty buff and it really hurt. I never did that again!

My buddy Dave lived about a half mile away; also on the bay. He lived in a much nicer house that I. Besides being bigger on a bigger lot, it also had a fine outdoor pool. We used the hell out of it during the summer. We decided we wanted to take off - why I don't know. We both had good lives. We took off hitchhiking to California. We got rides pretty well till we got to just outside of Roseburg Oregon, where a state bull pulled up to us, next to the highway. After questioning us he figured out we were lying about going to our granny's in Roseburg. He threw us in the juvy - first time I'd ever been there. I thought my dad was going to kill me when he and Mom picked me up to take me home, but surprisingly he didn't act mad. I think being a smart guy he decided that if I wasn't happy at home, it wouldn't work to punish me too much. Dave and I didn't get to hang with each other much after that.

When I started high school I joined the band playing trumpet at my dad's urging. I had some good times but soon

decided I wasn't the trumpet playing type. Of course my dad
was disappointed, but he got over it. I was driving him nuts
playing loud Fats Domino, Chuck Berry, Little Richard, and
Jerry Lee Lewis in my room by then. Reportedly Jerry Lee
Lewis got kicked out of England because he married his 13 year
old niece. We would, a few months later, see him live at the
local roller skating rink. He had long blond curly hair, and he
jumped up on the piano, and as he played, his hair fell farther
and farther down his face. There was a big rumble that night
with the local swabs; what a wild time that was! Sometimes
there was friction between locals and sailors. Some of the worst
at our high school were cruising town looking for drunk swabs to
roll.

I ended up becoming a reserve swab myself. My dad
and Dino's dad thought I needed a regimented life and got me
into the Seabee Reserve. I really didn't like the meetings and
drills, but I hung in there. I hung out with a guy we called
Maynard. He looked like Maynard Krebbs. When we went
through the gate after the meetings we ran to his car to avoid
being seen in our uniform. The reserve was later a blessing as
they were just starting to talk about Viet Nam, and thought
something was going to happen, and I'd be sucked in.

I joined football, but after a broken wrist decided football
wasn't worth being injured over. I stayed with track, but was
never good enough to letter, but it kinda got me a girl - Jan. She
was pretty and had huge knockers. She liked jocks and I played
that card as long as I could. I still didn't have a car, and had to
double date with a buddy that had wheels. It made it real hard to
get close with her, but I think she liked it that way. She only let
me cop a feel once in a while.   Ken and I started playing what

we called "the Liquor Store Game". We hung in sight of the
liquor store, and when someone went to their car, we waited till
they left, then swiped the liquor. We were rolling in liquor; we
had so much we even sold it out of my locker at school. We told
a friend we called the "Beast" about it, and he came along one
eve. The customer left the store with a whole box of liquor and
put it in his car, but he locked it. That didn't stop the "Beast" as
he just kicked the window in, and we grabbed the bottles, and
took off. We called him the "Beast" because he was stocky and
tough, and did pushups at school with other students standing on
his back - good guy to have as a friend, but that incident made
the "Liquor Store Game" too hot afterward and we did it no
more.

My senior year, because I had taken six courses and no
study hall previously, I had only one class - wood shop. I had a
lot of time on my hands, and thought about the old NAD having
everything made of copper and brass. Evidently when they built
the base they put brass tops on all the tables, and big unsheathed
copper cables in every building to ground them. Even the
machinery had copper and brass because it wouldn't spark, and
set off ammunition. I knew it was a gold mine, and set off to
hygrade it. I took an open boat over and filled it up, and brought
it back to my folk's house. I did all this under the cover of
darkness and my folks never knew. I worked as a caretaker for
a lady down the road, so my folks didn't think it odd when I had
money. I took the hygrading to a salvage yard downtown, and
sold it to a guy named Benny. He kind of hid it for me in the
bottom of the barrel. Once I got greedy and put so much metal
in the open row boat that it sank in waves coming back, and I
had to swim about half way back. I had so much money I

sometimes wore suits to school and paid kids to carry stuff for me, and until I got a car sometimes took taxis to school.
I bought a car from Myna and Harvey, our previous neighbors. It was a 48 Ford coupe with a 6 cylinder, and of course bought it without my folk's permission. Harvey being the good guy he was, didn't say anything to my folks. I met this guy called "Wimp" and we decided to take a road trip; so we took off going south. We ended up at my uncle's house in Aberdeen, Curt Cobain's home town. My uncle helped me get the car running better. We managed to get busted for stealing gas. Since it was our family home town, it didn't go down well in the family, and my stepdad's mom came down to the jail to get me out. She was saying "Joe it's all right", but I knew underneath she was mad. I had to sell the car.

Our battalion had to go to Port Hueneme to train for two weeks. It got me out of school for 2 weeks, so I liked that part. Most of the trip was boring military crap, but on my only weekend there myself and a couple of buddies, I met there, went on Saturday afternoon to the local park. It was jamming there, as there was a band on the stage, dressed in red and white striped shirts. They sounded great and played surfing songs. I'd never heard anything like it before.

On a later drill with my battalion, we went to Sandpoint Naval Air Station to pour cement. It was just a weekend drill. Usual junk, except one eve a guy came around and informed us that anyone that wanted could go up in a A3 - I think it was called. It had the funny thing sticking out the front of it. Anyway of course I held my hand up, and could hardly believe no one wanted to go - you kidding me? I was kinda scared, not being one that likes heights, but I toughed it out. I about crapped my pants when we did a barrel roll. We went over to the Idaho border up to Neah Bay and back over to Sandpoint in about 45 minutes. What a rush taking off - sucks you right back in your seat. This was a powerful jet.

Well I'd been a pretty good guy for a while so my dad said "I could get wheels". He threw in a few bucks, but I had most of the money. My dad picked out a 49 Chevy with a six cylinder - a really boring car, but I found a 50 Olds coupe with a V-8 in it, and that's what I bought. It turned out to be a good choice in the long run, because I had to work on that car so much, I got savvy at wrenching, and at 18, rebuilt the motor using a book and managed to successfully complete the rebuild. It smoked a bit, but was a pretty midnight blue hardtop with likewise interior. It was a chick magnet.

I met a guy from P.A. named Hank. He was a beer drinking, fun loving, stocky, good looking sort of guy. He was in a different Navy reserve unit. He told me he was dating this girl - Martha, and that she had a sister named Sally. They were great, good looking girls, and even after Hank got busted on top of her by her folks, and lost that girl, I continued to see Sally. She was the prettiest of the sisters. Hank and I spent some time together in P.A. Hank used to put his reserve uniform on, and go into stores and buy our beer. On one occasion Hank was in a store getting our beer, when some punk that knew Hank told the clerk that he was just 18 years old. Hank waited outside the back door until the punk came out, then he "drilled him".

Hank and I were partying out of my car, and we had no money for gas, so we went out, and got busted for swiping gas. It was starting to look like I was going to keep getting busted.

The band I had seen in Port Hueneme was called "The Beach Boys". Of course they made a lot of good songs suited to those times! Later there were stories about one of the Beach Boys staying in his room for a year then wrote a song about it called "In My Room".

I got my high school diploma, but didn't go to my graduation ceremony. Pat and I had a party to go to - to the disappointment of my parents. They eventually got over it and so did I.

CHAPTER 5

SEABEE

A few days later I was shipping out to active duty for two years, and really wasn't into it except I was traveling anyway. My dad gave me a ride to the ferry. I guess it was supposedly a "manly thing to do". I felt pretty dorky walking on the ferry with my "swabby suit" on and my sea bag strapped over my shoulder; then on to the airport bound for Treasure Island.

Treasure Island is a stop on the way to your duty station, so I was only there for about two months, but had some really good adventures in Frisco.

I hung with one of my aunts - Norma. Norma wasn't a real pretty woman, but she had a great funny personality, and I loved being around her. She was a maid in a hotel and it turned out the Beatles were her tenants. She said she could get me a concert ticket as she didn't want to go. Of course I jumped at that chance. They were a fairly new band and I didn't know much about them, but could tell they were going to be great. I went to the concert and it was great, except the "teeny boppers" started screaming through the whole concert. I really couldn't hear the songs that well and felt like slapping some of them. I kept telling them to shut up to no end. Anyway I always felt privileged to have seen the Beatles!

A few weeks later I went to the Cow Palace to see Eric Burden and the Animals. They were dressed in these black waiter looking suits that really looked "mickey mouse". They played "House of the Rising Sun", and about halfway through the song a bunch of "bubble gummers" ran up on stage, and started tearing Eric Burden's clothes off. The cops being so outnumbered started swinging their billy clubs and the girls were soon flying off the stage; and of course Eric and the band never missed a beat through it all.

I had a great experience at Treasure Island when Hank, my buddy from P.A. showed up, and got to hang with him for a few weeks. I spent time in "Frisco" with my aunt and Hank. My aunt and Hank were naturals together. After a while we were both shipped out. But in the meantime I had a nose bleed that would not stop, and thought I was going to bleed to death. They cured it for good, as they cauterized it, essentially burned the veins out of my nose with a soldering iron looking thing. Hurt like hell when the drugs wore off, but it sure worked. I always looked real bad in a fight, because my nose bled everywhere. It always looked like I got beat pretty bad, even when I won the fight.

CHAPTER 6

AMPHIB BASE

The military decided to send me to the Amphib Base in Coronado California. What sweet duty that was. The base sits on the Silver Strand between I.B. and Coronado. Very comfortable there and the base is palm trees, one end to the other. At this time a dude had to take a ferry to get there from San Diego. Now there is a big bridge. I.B. is close to the border, so Mexico was doable.

I got assigned to the Motor Pool as a grunt. Most of the guys there were lifers, but I did meet some other young guys. One of them was Digger Odell, a kind of oakey dude from Oklahoma. He wasn't a good looking guy, in fact he was sort of funny looking, but he turned out to be a stand-up good friend - except once.

We went to T.J. a lot, and drugs and drink were easy to find there. It was easy to get pot, which I had messed with a little in high school; bennies, and tequila also filled the bill. Horseshit cigarettes were also available, but I really wanted nothing to do with the foul things. We hung at the Bat Club, a night club on Revoluccion Ave. One night when myself, Digger, and a couple of others from the base were there drinking, a guy told us we could go down the street and see a donkey with a chick. My buddies went, but I didn't want to see it, and the way they described it when they returned, I was really glad I didn't go!

My buddies and I were walking a side street up to

Revoluccion Ave on the way to the Bat club, when a Federaly stopped me and informed me he was taking me to jail. I asked "Why" and he said "for walking with a known whore on the city streets. I was on the end of the line of buddies, and there was a Mexican chick walking next to me, but I didn't know her, and hadn't even said word one to her! The cop was clearly setting me up, but I couldn't protest enough to do anything about it. He threw me in the T.J. jail, while my buddies dug up the money to get me out. What a hole! It is just a concrete room with no bunk or anything just a hole in the middle of the floor to relieve myself in. There wasn't even any toilet paper unless I asked for it; they must have thought I would hang myself with it, ha ha. Fortunately my pals got the money together pretty fast and I have never been so happy to get out of a place.

The Coasters showed up at the Club one night and sang "Charlie Brown" and a couple of other good songs. It was the second time I saw them, as they played in the Animals show at the Cow Palace. I smoked some pot in T.J. but the bennies were what I bought the most. They could keep me up and going. Tequila was so cheap I got whacked a lot on it and got into trouble for returning to the base messed up. Seemed like I spent about half my time in the military on restriction.

The base was the home of the Underwater Demolition Team as well as seals. The UDT was the buffest guys I had ever seen. Only a hand full of men make it through the rigorous training to get into UDT. I saw firsthand the hard time those guys got. They had to go out on the water for many hours hanging off the side of a big life raft. Then they had to crawl around in the sand on the beach with their rifle. They got so raw in the crotch from the sand, they could hardly walk. They had to march everywhere with that raft on their heads, and if they screwed up at all they had to do a hundred or more push-ups then fall back in. Once after three days and nights awake, swimming, marching, crawling etc. they were told they would be allowed to lay down and sleep. After they lay for a few minutes, the petty officers came in and threw firecrackers around, and turned over their bunks, and up and out the door they went to continue their training for who knows how much longer. Later I heard, they were the baddest to fight in Vietnam. When I was on base security later on, I wouldn't go into their barracks. I could just get one of them to come outside and let them handle any situation.

I decided to buy a car and got a 50 Ford coupe which was a good looking car with mohair interior. Right after I got it I noticed it was going through water. I took it into the shop on base and put a new set of head gaskets on it; but just couldn't get it fixed. It just kept overheating. I used it for a while, and could get "bennies" from T.J. and party all weekend, and it definitely helped get chicks. A lot of underage chicks came down to T.J. because they could drink there. I got tired of the problems with the Ford and got rid of it. It just wasn't a dependable ride.

There were some good things going on in San Diego and one of them was an outdoor concert at a stadium. The main act was Peter and Gordon with a couple of other acts. Peter and Gordon were typical Brits and I really wasn't that jazzed on the concert, but I had fun anyway, and met a pretty young thing I got to spend some time with. Carol King was in the show and we both enjoyed her.

I got pretty loose, and that night when I got back to the barracks I was feeling pretty sick when I lay down. The barf started coming and I grabbed the nearest thing to barf in. A guy across from me just bought a pair of "Beatles boots" and I filled one of them up and put it back. The next morning he was steaming and asked me "if I saw anyone wandering around there the night before"? I lied and said "no". He was really pissed and didn't want to get in a brawl with him when I had such a hangover.

The next day was a sad day in American history, JFK had been assassinated and the whole base was in lock down. No one in or out. He was one of the most beloved presidents of all time, and it surely made me very sad. It seemed unreal how anyone could do, that or even get away with it. It still has me wondering how the assassin is killed before he can even get questioned. Seems like a lot of cover up went on there.

I was kind of a screw-up so they decided to put me in the galley as a punishment. It really back fired as myself, and a couple of guys, got an apartment in 1.B, and took lots of food from the galley for our apartment. I went over to the motor pool and lay a little food out to get a pickup, then loaded the bed up with food and drove it right out the front gate. Some of the screw offs in the galley even ran around throwing eggs at each other. A couple of times when I made a big bowl of salad, I came back and found butt prints in it, and had to toss it out and start all over. There was talk of one of the cooks boning the hams; it was a good thing I ate off base mostly.

Imperial Beach was a good place to have an apartment because I was getting into surfing a bit, and it had decent surf. It was a good way to fit in, as swabs usually didn't surf. A guy named Culver and his wife had the place next door. I liked both of them, and I felt bad when he got kicked out of the service. I saw him a few months later on a Harley Hog in a biker gang with a sleazy whore on the back. I guess his marriage ended when he got kicked out of the military, and had too much time on his hands.

I finally got out of the mess hall and back to the motor pool. After a brief stint running a street sweeper, they put me on security patrol. At first I was on foot patrol wearing a helmet, and a billy club, patrolling a portion of the base. Then I was assigned to patrol the Silver Strand with a jeep. It was great fun. I could strap down my helmet and put the jeep in four wheel drive, and chase rabbits over the sand dunes.

A big cargo ship had caught fire, and either drifted or was pushed into the beach on the Silver Strand. My job was to patrol that section of beach during the day. It was packed with spectators who wanted to watch the ship full of cotton burn. There were many young, pretty girls, on the beach, and I used the opportunity to invite them into my jeep for a ride on the beach. I usually had two or three girls in the jeep with me, hoping of course to get to know some of them. I did some, and spent time with them on later dates. This was clearly against the rules and I could hardly believe I didn't get busted for it. Eventually I was taken off jeep patrol on the strand, because on one of my night patrols, I strapped on my helmet, put it in four wheel drive, and went chasing rabbits on the dunes. I ran it pretty hard, and it started running bad. The transmission was messing up, and I just barely rolled in neutral, into the main gate, as it wouldn't go into gear anymore. I logged out and didn't say anything. The jeep sat for a couple of days, so they couldn't tell for sure who used it last, so I didn't get busted - but they thought I had done it and put me back on foot patrol on the base.

After playing pool with Digger I went to my bunk to turn in, because my buddies and I had to give up our place in 1.B. About 1 a.m. the two brothers who bunked just down from me came in drunk. These two argued and fought constantly. They crawled in to their bunks. A short time later the one in the top bunk gurgled a little, and the brother in the lower bunk stuck his head out of the side; looked up and said "you all right?" Just then the brother in the top bunk barfed in the face of the one below. He got up and dragged the other one down and they started wrestling and fighting on the floor, barf and all. Everyone couldn't laugh hard enough because these two were such clowns anyway.

I knew relatives were in the area, and decided to go visit my aunt, uncle, and cousins. They were spread between Torrance and Gardena. I went to Torrance first to visit Uncle Frank, Aunt Hazel, and Cousin Todd. I had a pleasant few days stay, but was not impressed at all with Todd. He was quite a wimp, so I didn't hang with him much, and left. I tried to find one of my other cousins, who had visited my family in Bennington. He was very cool, and showed up with a nice Corvette. I finally had found Rod and he told me we should visit Hollywood Boulevard. We went there and managed to talk our way into the Whiskey-A-Go-Go. Johnny Rivers was playing that night - we couldn't believe our luck! It was quite the place as there were two glass cages, suspended in the air, on each side of the stage. There was a go-go dancer in each, grinding away. It was the coolest thing I had done to that point, and we finished off the night with some more drinking. He dropped me off at another cousin's house in Gardena.

My Cousin Marin was just a little older than I, and was married to an older guy named Gino. I instantly liked them both and their little kids, and stayed with them a couple of days. I sensed Marin wouldn't stay married to Gino, because of their age difference, and was right, they broke up a couple of months later. I found out at a later date that there was to be a political rally in San Francisco, and took off hitch-hiking to Frisco. I got a ride from a familiar looking guy in a very nice white Ford convertible. I realized a ways through the short ride - mainly one on ramp to another, a few miles away, that it was Cesar Romero, a movie star at the time. I didn't let on that I knew who he was, and we had a good conversation. He was a very happy go-lucky guy and I enjoyed the talk with him. He dropped me off, and I decided to take a bus from there. I found the bus stop, got on, and sat next to a pretty brunette about my age, who introduced herself as Dianne McFarland. She claimed she was the sister of Spanky McFarland, one of the kids on the Our Gang comedies. I didn't know for sure if she was lying, but she seemed genuine - I would find out at a later date, she was.

After spending an hour with her on the bus, I got her phone number and went on my way to the rally. I wanted to go to the Barry Goldwater rally. He was the Republican Presidential candidate and I heard there would be other celebrities there. It was held in downtown Frisco among the tall buildings; which all had an armed Secret Service agent on top. The crowd was being cruised by other obvious agents in their sunglasses, and bulging suits. Dick Van Dyke came on and spoke for a while, then Goldwater came on to boos and cheers.

His campaign slogan was "In your heart you know he's right",
but there were also signs that said "In your guts you know he's
nuts". I thought he was kind of nuts, tired of his speech, and left.
It seemed dangerous to rally among the tall buildings. My leave
was over, and when I returned to the base, they had a new job for
me. I was to run the dozer at the base dump. It seemed they
were giving me a better job than I deserved, and I soon found out
why. It was a dangerous job because sometimes I ran over
containers of fuel, chemicals, etc. that would ignite. It would
flame on and I had to jump off and grab the fire extinguisher and
put the dozer out - some job! On a good note, they had beer
machines on the base that sold cans of beer for a quarter. I had a
lot of slack time on that job, so I drank some of that beer. A guy
named Green ratted me out, and I ended up kicking his ass at the
barracks one night after confronting him. Cousin Marin,
divorced by now moved to San Diego. I had bought a 56 Chevy
hardtop by then. I replaced the motor; put in a four speed
transmission, and painted the car. It was a real beauty. I decided
to try to set Digger up with Marin. The three of us got in my car,
and went out drinking at a bar we could get into, because I was
still underage. After the bar we went out to a nice view spot
above El Cajon to drink some more. I left for a while to give
Digger and Marin some time alone. I didn't realize how
depraved Digger really was, as I heard screams and had to go
back to my car and drag Digger off Marin. I realized some of the
oakies just were overwhelmed by the thought of time alone with
a woman; anyway I threatened him, and we took Marin back to
her apartment. Digger apologize to her before we went back to
the barracks.

I met a couple of guys during my time in the galley;

Saftey and Red. Saftey was a tall good time Charlie sort of guy, while Red was a more serious, tough, red headed guy. We could get 22 rifles and go out to the desert beyond El Cajon, and shoot rabbits and camp. We became partners in a lending money for interest scheme, also called a "slush fund". We lent money at fifty percent interest due the next payday. Soon we had a few thousand dollars in it, and were bringing down a lot of money. Well it was just too good to last, and it didn't. They sent some C.I.A. agents on to the base to investigate us, and busted us red handed. We all got special court martial, and were found guilty. I was sent to Presidio Stockade for a couple of months; I never saw Saftey or Red again, and don't know what happened to them. I had to clean bilges of ships for hard duty during the day, and be confined at night. The Marine guards were tough, but I kept to myself and got through it okay. Oddly they never busted me down in grade. I was a construction man when I went in and a construction man when I got out.

I returned to the base to a letter from my family. I never told them about my bust. My dad wrote that the Beatles, when they were there, stayed at the Edgewater Inn in Seattle, and when they left, the management pulled up the carpet; cut it into one inch pieces, and sold it for a dollar a piece as carpet the Beatles stood on. They sold enough to pay for new carpet and more, as "Beatle Mania" was really ramping up. The Edgewater Inn was also where Frank Zappa stayed when he played Seattle. It is on a pier over Puget Sound and Frank fished from the window and caught a mud shark and wrote a song "Mud Shark". I got shipped out to Travis AFB to be shipped out to a permanent duty station. I had time to kill there, so I gave Dianne McFarland a call. She told me to meet her at a restaurant in L.A. called

"Spankys". I went there and sure enough Dianne was there, as she worked for her brother at the restaurant. She really showed me a good time. First I met Spanky who by then was a big fat guy who owned two restaurants - Spankys and Fattys. He had a nice little place on Redondo Beach, and Dianne lived with him. We went to a lot of beach parties, and got to surf the area some. Dianne was very social and even though I was a lowly swab, she treated me like a good friend, but like all things it was over because I had to return to Travis to be shipped out to who knows where?

Travis AFB was just a transfer point for me, and there really wasn't much there. Victorville was nearby, but it really didn't have anything for me except a few bars that didn't interest me. I didn't know anyone in the area. I had taken a bunch of time off there and didn't realize I was using up my leave. When I checked in they informed me I was leaving the next day for Okinawa, and MCB5 a Seabee battalion. I thought I would be going by military aircraft, but that was not the case, because I was going by Pan Am Airlines by way of Hawaii. When I reached Hawaii I loved the place, and wanted to return when I could stay awhile. I only had a six hour layover, and used it to see as much as possible of Oahu. I went directly to Honolulu and walked and swam at Waikiki Beach. I didn't want to leave except for the adventure that lay ahead. I bought a pint of vodka and headed for the plane. No problem getting it on the plane. There was not the security in 1964 that we have today. The stewardesses were very nice to me and gave me all the orange juice I wanted. Big mistake for them, because I drank up the whole pint, and got sick and couldn't get to the barf bag in time and barfed all over the area. I woke up hours later, me and my area all cleaned up. I couldn't apologize enough to the stewardesses, and fortunately they didn't hold it against me. To this day I can't drink vodka. After flying a third of the way around the world we arrived at Sukaran on Okinawa. When I got to the door on the plane, I about fell over when I breathed my first breath of that thick, muggy air. I knew instantly this was going to be a different experience than I had ever encountered before.

CHAPTER 7

OKINAWA

A jeep was there to pick me up, and we went about halfway across the island to a little base in the middle of the island called Camp Kinser. It was kind of odd. There were no fences around the base, just a road through it with a gate at each end. It was the home of Mobil Construction Battalion 5 (MCB5) and a few scattered men from other battalions. There were only about six or seven hundred men there.

I reported to my company and was assigned to a Quonset hut. I barely got my stuff put away when a guy came along. His name was West and he had a lot of hostility toward the military and me already. He started grilling me about who I was; where I was from, how long I had been in etc.? I could tell the other guys were listening, so I did my best to hold my own. It was all more important to him, because I didn't like the military life, and just wanted to do my time and get out. I could hear other guys in the barracks smirking a bit, and knew we had an audience. Fortunately West decided I definitely wasn't a lifer and walked on - I was officially inducted into the company. Slowly but surely I met most of the other guys in the company. Heeter Brothers - one was a petty officer, the other a younger construction man from Georgia. They really had the southern drawl, and were amusing to listen to. Mays was a stocky tough guy with a sort of distain toward everyone and everything. I liked a guy named Plankey a lot. He was sort of slow, easy going, probably from somewhere in the middle USA. I liked a guy named Polcari the best. He was an Italian descended guy, who was never serious about anything, and mostly a joker. Unfortunately he managed to get me in trouble with the brass right away. We were standing at attention in the center isle during a Quonset inspection, when Polcari started smirking and joking in a low voice. The lieutenant heard him and looked back. I couldn't help myself and was smiling - well the lieutenant saw me and thought I was the wise guy. I got reprimanded for it, and had to do the base restriction - oh well! I learned to be careful around Polcari from then on. We were building some barracks over at Camp Hansen, a Marine base. I was to work with a couple of lifers on concrete. These two, one named Logy because he drank lots of loganberry wine, and the other called Les. They would get drunk as a skunk in the evening, but really knew concrete when it came time to work. I really learned a trade from them that came in handy in my civilian life.

The military really made it easy to become a drunk, as the Canteen had sixteen ounce beer for ten cents a can, after work. So for under a buck we could get completely shit faced. We would start there then go to Koza or New Koza and drink more and fight. Usually Seabees, Marines, and the few swabs that came into Naha fought everyone else. Of course Seabees and Marines hung together because Seabees were Marine trained. We wore Marine fatigues; had weapons and had Marines attached to our company. I ended up with some good Marine friends. I was an A-gunner on an M-60 machine gun. M-60's had an A-gunner, an ammo carrier, and a barrel changer.

I pulled the trigger of course; the ammo carrier carried the ammo; and the barrel changer changed barrels with big heat resistant gloves. The barrels turned hot and could be twisted out and a cool one put in in seconds. In the movies a guy sprays the enemy with unlimited volleys of lead, but that is not the way it really works. The barrels turn cherry red, and the gun will malfunction or not even fire, or blow up if the barrel gets too hot. They are fired in short to medium bursts to keep the barrel from getting to hot. If the barrel is too hot, the barrel changer will twist a cool barrel in. We couldn't believe how much damage an M-60 could do. It was impressive.

It didn't take long to figure out why the air was so heavy and muggy - it rained a lot; almost all the time. You might think I would get used to it quickly, being from the Northwest, where it rains a lot, but in the Northwest the rain is much more comfortable. The difference is the heat.

I was put on night security patrol and really got sick of the warm, muggy rain every watch. My patrol was on foot at the junior officer's quarters. I decided to have some fun, to relieve the boredom, so I went over to the back of the mess hall and swiped some eggs. Eggs came in layers of twelve by twelve. I put a bandana on and ran through the junior officers Quonset door, slinging as many eggs as possible while at a run, at officers in bed, and out the other door, and disappear. I never got caught doing it, but they knew who was doing it and they were really putting the pressure on me to fess up. They responded by taking me out of the company and putting me in the galley. I really didn't mind. At least it wasn't out in that miserable rain, with a slicker on. Things were cheap in Okinawa, and I bought a sweet Sony tape recorder, and set it up it in the chow hall during meals.

Mostly everyone liked the tunes. There was one particularly strange lifer, because he had no tongue. It wasn't a pretty sight watching him eat because he drooled constantly - poor slob!

There was an Oki local that came by each day to get the garbage cans full of old produce etc., probably for his pigs. I started putting big rocks in the bottom of the cans - it was hilarious watching him trying to put those heavy cans in his truck. He figured out who was doing it, and once when I was walking in Koza, I saw him walking down the other side of the street. As soon as he saw me he started karate chopping his hand toward me, like he was going to chop me.

Sometimes a man just needs some female company, and I got a girlfriend in New Koza. She was probably other guy's girlfriend, but I didn't mind. She looked young, and I was shocked to learn she was actually fifty, and she actually had some boobs not very common for the locals. Most G.I. wanted "Round Eye" American girls mostly because of that. "Round Eyes" were very hard to find because they were almost always military brats.

I was always an avid water skier and found there was a cove on the island where we could ski. Polcari, Plankey, and I went down there a few times. It was a little scary, because the water was clear and we could see big tiger sharks below, while we skied over them. It was real good incentive to not fall! One liberty a few of us decided to go to Naha - the biggest city on Okinawa. It was an old, kinda dingy place, with very narrow streets. The "Skoshy Cabs" "hauled ass" at break neck speed down these streets. It made me so nervous, I jumped out of the cab at a stop, paid, and told the guys I would walk. They also must have not liked the ride either, because they also jumped

out. We didn't realize how dangerous walking in Naha really
was until we were told later. We looked around at the markets,
which had everything. We had a few beers in clubs, which
were as dead as it was during the day. We heard about the
opium dens and went out of our way to find one.

It was a sort of non-descript place on the outside, sort of
off by itself. We liked the looks of the inside. We were met by
two beautiful girls in Geisha attire when we entered. Polcari had
one by the arm and was on his way to the cushions with her
straight away. We were served Saki right away - a rice brew that
I learned to like. We usually had Saki in our lockers on the base,
right next to the light bulb in our lockers, because of the
humidity. Saki is drank warm. Soon a guy came in with a long
pipe and the opium. It tasted crappy but sure got us high. One
of our guys wouldn't touch it, but the rest of us sure did. These
places were of course off-limits. One of the girls showed us a
panel that came off the wall to reveal a hidden tiny passageway,
where they could stash us if the SP came along. By the time we
got done there, we had to take a cab, because we could hardly
walk.

The good thing about Camp Kinser was because there
was no fence around it, a "skoshy cab" could drive right up to
the jungle perimeter of the base, and we could stumble to our
barracks.

Another form of entertainment was the concerts at the
club at Sukaran - an Air Force base not far away. There were a
couple of local girls that sang hit songs with a band that played
there a lot. They were stunningly beautiful, and I went to see
them often with a buddy named Bailey. Bailey eventually got
busted stealing stuff at the camp out of people's lockers. I

wondered how he was able to always have money to spend when he was just a peon like me. Anyway he was busted and was shipped out to the brig at Camp Hansen.

Our battalion and Marine unit were scheduled for war games in the jungle. While firing my M-60 a local was right next to me with a gunnysack collecting my shell casings to turn in for the scrap money. It made it real hard to take the games seriously, of course we were issued blanks. We could put a flare casing on the barrel of an M-16 and shoot it a long way up in the air, and almost hit the wing of a small recon plane. Our lieutenant saw me. After the camping in the mud ended, I was restricted to the base again. I even did a bit of time in the brig at Camp Hansen, and all this was getting kind of old, so I decided to clean up my act before I got kicked out. I didn't clean up my act long as I went on a Saki binge in New Koza, and on my return to Camp Kinser fell head on into a binjo ditch. Because of the enormous amount of rain, Okinawa had six foot deep ditches on each side of the back roads to handle all the water - called binjo ditches. Since the ditches were covered with slime and I'd fallen in, I was also covered. A second class named Eslick, who had a room of his own at one end of our Quonset hut, had just bought a nice, new silk blanket, and had placed it on his bed. I came in drunk, and he wasn't there, so I proceeded to wallow in my filth all over his new blanket. Fortunately my buds grabbed me, threw me in the shower, and I passed out in bed. No one ratted me out, because no one really liked this guy anyway. In fact at a later date, Plankey got into a fight with Eslick, and most everyone including Mays was yelling "Get him Plankey"! It ended in a draw, but Plankey's stock with the guys went up. Eslick's went even lower.

Another fight that occurred started with a young, buff southern guy walking through the barracks stabbing lockers with a bayonet, yelling how much he "hated niggers" and how he wanted to "kill them". We pretty much thought he was just a jerk, and told him to sleep it off. He didn't and he went down to a first class Petty Officer's room at the end of the Quonset. He picked a fight with the black first class and the first class kicked his ass. What came next impressed me to this day. The black first class apologized to us all for getting into a fight with the idiot. We all accepted his apology with a rousing ovation and said "you had nothing to apologize for and we wished we had kicked the idiot's ass, and saved the first class the trouble. That incident was very bonding, and a morale booster for our battalion. The first class got reprimanded slightly, and life at the barracks moved on.

I was hanging in the barracks one day after work - listening to the Four Seasons and Lou Cristy. For some reason guys that sang like girls were real popular then, and that is what Armed Forces Radio played. Sometimes they played Stones, Beatles and Kinks, but not very often. Armed Forces Station kinda resisted early psychedelic music, as it might rot our minds. Someone said "West has a live 3.5 rocket launcher round". The 3.5 rocket launcher replaced the bazooka. I went outside to watch. West loaded it, and blasted an old jeep on the blocks that was being parted out. We couldn't believe how much damage it did. That jeep flew about five meters off the ground and came down looking like a crumpled beer can. Later I was relieved of the M-60 and given a 3.5 rocket launcher, but never had any live rounds. I took it in the shower with me, cleaned it with a toilet brush, and then oiled it daily.

I had a chance to take an R + R (Rest and Relaxation) to Japan, and took it. It was on a military cargo plane with a few seats on it. It landed on a military base there, and after checking into the quarters I went out on the town with Plankey, who also managed to talk his way there.

The first time I saw Tokyo, it reminded me of an ant hill. Seemed everyone was going about their way with a purpose and everyone had a job to do for the good of all. It looked like it was real glittery, and I was glad Tokyo hadn't been extensively bombed during WW II. We recognized that we had to behave ourselves here. After returning to the base, chow, and clean up, we headed out again. We were told Sumo wrestling matches were a lot of fun, and we were told right! We found a match in a Tokyo suburb and paid our way in. So far the Japanese seemed real nice, sort of reserved, but that wasn't the case inside. There was a guy up there pumping everyone up, course we didn't know what he was saying, but he was getting everyone pumped up. Then the wrestlers, referee, and announcer came out, and the place really got wild. It looked like one of the wrestlers was local, and the crowd favorite. As it got started it seemed a lot like a boxing match in America, but way more exciting. We started hooting for the local wrestler, and it seemed those around us were treating us like locals. They were jumping up; so we did; they were high-fiving; so we did it with them. We were getting slapped in the back and even given a bit of Saki. All in all it was one of the best events we had ever attended, and a great way to hang with the locals. The Japanese are incredibly into their wrestling. It ended up being the best thing we did in Japan. Tokyo because of Mount Fuji in the background reminded me of Seattle with Mount Rainier in the background. I got a little homesick in that moment since I hadn't seen home for quite some time. Speaking of home - I bought my mom a set of Noritake china, and had it sent to her while there. Our home had a big bamboo plant next to it, so I bought a 12 place set with bamboo on it; shipping and all for thirty two dollars. An incredible deal. My mom always loved that china, which she eventually gave to my daughter.

About this time I quit smoking, and haven't smoked tobacco again. It put me on edge some, but I took up gum chewing to replace smoking. It worked like a charm, but I had jaws like a bull dog from chewing so much gum. It was harder to quit chewing gum, than quitting smoking tobacco. I had a rough throat from a cold when I quit smoking, so tobacco tasted bad which helped make quitting easier.

Mays, Plankey and I heard there was a Saki brewery on Okinawa. We got the location and took a cab there. From the start we couldn't believe how dirty the place was. We saw rat droppings everywhere and even a dead rat on top of a beam that ran over the top of the open vat. We wondered how many rats had fallen into the open vat. We all decided right there not to drink any Saki made on the island. It was enough to gag a maggot.

There was a sugar refinery on the island because there was a lot of sugar cane. I didn't realize that brown sugar was just raw sugar that hadn't had the molasses spun out of it centrifugally. It was quite a lot cleaner place than the Saki brewery was. We went to New Koza and finished the day drinking. I left the bar and went to my girlfriend Aiko's apartment for the night. We had Cinderella Liberty that meant we were supposed to be back by midnight, but because our camp had no fence around it, I had a cab take me to the fringe of the base. Then I went in and changed just in time to make 6 a.m. muster.

A buddy of mine told me an R & R to Hong Kong was possible. We jumped at the chance to go to China. The flight was on a cargo plane again, and I'll never forget Hong Kong from the air as we approached. It seemed most people lived on Sampans and other boats, rafts, piers on the water. I've been back a half dozen times over recent years, and it looks totally different. Now Hong Kong is high rises end to end. And very modern. I got a chance to go to Victory Hill, a great view spot above the city. We also went to this huge floating village that was Hong Kong's water front. The Chinese seemed like good hard working people, and even though we were in an unprotected area, we never felt threatened. This place had everything for sale, but I really had no money, or desire to buy. I've visited Hong Kong on recent dive trips, and still feel pretty safe there.

On my return to Camp Kinser, the place was all a buzz. Seems our battalion was being sent to Viet Nam. The macho guys in the Battalion were all bragging how they couldn't wait to kill some Gooks, but I wanted no part of it, and got toe to toe with some of the guys arguing over it. Polcari, Plankey, Mays, and some of my other buddies were either neutral or didn't want any part of it like me. We loaded up and set out. Seems our mission was to work on a landing strip near the Mekong Delta. We were relieved to learn we would have a perimeter of our Marine detachment, and were pretty much out of harm's way. We were transported by way of C135 Cargo planes that had been fitted with seats that faced backward. When we arrived, we were

bussed out to our project, and set up squad tents for quarters. I
thought Okinawa was muggy, but this was far worse. I
immediately didn't like the place at all, and figured out a scheme
to get out of there. I only had about four months of service left
but wanted to get away sooner than that. I heard one of our
ships, the "Turner Joy", was attacked at night in the Gulf of
Tonkin by a North Vietnamese gunboat. To this day no one on
the crew, even the Captain, could swear he had seen the gunboat.
Maybe it was a case of itchy trigger finger. It seemed like the
U.S. was just itching to go to war; to what end I don't know!

        I had only been shot at once and the shooter was so far
away, he couldn't possibly hit me. I decided to get a letter off to
my mom. She was friends with the local college dean, and I
asked her to get him to send a letter to MCB5 telling them I was
accepted to Summer College. Since I was far from a good
soldier, they might let me out a little early, and the gamble paid
off. They let me out two weeks later. They shipped me out the
way I had come in; full combat gear, facing backwards, in a C-
135. This time we stopped briefly in Honolulu on the way to
Port Hueneme. I didn't know anyone on the plane, because there
were guys from other battalions, and Marines aboard. Port
Hueneme and Oxnard area looked pretty good, even though it
wasn't a pretty area, because I knew I'd be out of the service
within a couple weeks.

        As soon as I returned I went over to my buddy Gates
house and got my nice 56 Chevy hardtop back. Gates had let me
store it there while I was gone. I took off to my aunt and uncles
in Torrance, for a while. Frank was a good guy who had lived in
the area since he moved there when he was a kid. He had a good
pest control business, and was very generous. I heard him many

times complaining about the lack of law in the area, and thought he was ready to move on. Torrance had gangs of kids looting and marauding. No one was safe, and after a week or so I went back to Port Hueneme.

When I returned I was detained at the main gate, because I had been A.W.O.L. for a few days. They made me sit there for a few hours to sweat me out, but then they handed me my papers and said I was done. I was to go get my property and get off the base. They really didn't want me in the service, and once again it paid off. However they informed me I was to get a General Discharge; and I could have cared less! I grabbed my sea-bag, civies, and out the gate I went. I drove a free man.

CHAPTER 8

FREE

I stopped and got gas, and because there was a gas war going on, paid a whopping seventeen cents a gallon for gas. The first thing I did was to push my sea-bag out the window of my car on the freeway, and off to home I went.

I was in a hurry to get back, but also wanted to see the West Coast, so I decided to take the Pacific Coast Highway home. It was well worth it as the coast was beautiful. I stayed on the coast all the way to the Washington border, then took the freeway the rest of the way home. When I passed the Cowlitz River I noticed a bunch of guys standing in the water, so I went over to see what's up. Turned out they were dipping smelt with nets. Smelt are a small fish like sardines or grunion. They were getting a lot, and one of the guys gave me a half bucket of the little fish. I was really tired and crapped out there in my car. Late that evening I woke up and drove on and ended up in my brother Jan's driveway asleep early in the morning. My brother came out, woke me up, and welcomed me home. After hugging my brother's wife, rubbing my nieces and nephews head, we had breakfast, and I headed out for the rest of my life. I knew I was welcome at my folks, and decided to stay there for now. My mom and dad were fine, and my little brother was about seven, and a great kid. I decided to call him "Chopper", and he liked the name. Being a young, looking for adventure guy, I really didn't want to stay at my folks for long. I needed a job, and when I was in high school had passed the Navy Yard apprentice test. My dad by now was a boss there, and with all this I figured

I could get a job there. I was right, and got a job as a welder's helper, not exactly the job I wanted, but it would do. I had to go through welding school for six weeks, and got it no problem.

The Yard was building a couple of new ships. That's where I started, but after a while was moved inside a huge shop. It had huge doors at each end, and whole sections of ships were built here, and moved on railroad tracks by big cranes, out to the new ships, and attached. It was all pretty interesting at first, but when the work ran out, it got kinda boring. To offset the boredom I took all of this guy they called "Slow Mo's" welding gear, lunch bucket, and leathers over to this giant press, and flattened it into a giant pancake. Then since "Slow Mo" had been up in the bathroom all morning killing time, I put his stuff back without anyone noticing. He wasn't happy when he finally returned, but the other guys thought it was funny.

The big problem with working there for me was very little real work was available, so I would go help other welders using different methods of welding, and got into trouble for leaving my station. Talk about a day passing slowly, when there wasn't much to do, but I had to look busy!

I met Greg there, and we decided to get a place together. Greg was an only child brought up in a small town just across the water from the Yard. His folks owned a funeral home and Greg was kinda spoiled. Somehow he was able to talk a car salesman into selling him a new Chevy Nova with a 327 C V-8 with a four speed tranny. This car was fast as lightning, and it was real cool riding around in it. Even though my 56 Chev still looked good, his Nova hardtop was a real woman getter. They loved to ride around in it too.

Since I had just turned twenty one, I could legally buy liquor, and Greg liked it, because he was twenty. We got a little house across the highway from the Yard and the bay. We rented from a big fat old lady, that didn't mind renting to young guys. The place was no beauty, but we mostly partied there, and didn't care.

I met Cindy, a really beautiful blond girl who was just a bit overweight, but like I say "so pretty". I think she really liked hanging with me, because she had just divorced this guy after a short marriage, and he quit bothering her when I came on the scene. She only wanted to be buddies, and that was fine with me! I respected that, and except for an occasional kiss didn't push it.

I learned early that if I showed up at parties with a pretty girl, other girls there noticed and were interested in me.

Greg hung with different women, who soon tired of him, because he wouldn't act that interested. He did go out with one girl Becky that was of average beauty, good body, and huge boobs. Her breasts were so big she almost looked funny. He enjoyed showing up at parties with her, because everyone noticed her and her big "boobs" right away.

Greg had an open gas account at a local gas station. I had no money one night, and talked the guy at that station into putting a few gallons in my tank on his account. I forgot to tell Greg when I finally returned to our pad, and he found out later and got huffy about it. We ended up doing battle and he blacked my eye. We made up and decided to go drinking in his Nova. We ended up across the bay looking for a party. It had started snowing, and was getting pretty deep. He hit a road grader on the driver's side, and it peeled back the side like a can opener.

His car that was so nice looked like junk now. It didn't sink in to Greg as he was pretty drunk, and soon the cops showed up. They took us both to the station. Greg got thrown in jail for DWI, but I was cut loose, because they didn't have room for me at the jail.

Next day I got the money together and bailed him out. Greg still didn't seem to be concerned with his car, and cut all the wrecked sheet metal off with aviation snips and away we went to party some more.

Howie Green was a tough good looking blond guy I met at a friend's party. He was sort of a "froggy" guy that was always interested in a fight. He was from a notorious family that included eight boys - no girls. When a guy is raised in a family of eight boys, they all grow up tough. Even their dad was no slouch, because he walked out to the mailbox every day on his hands; put the paper in his mouth and walked back also on his hands. He and all his sons had arms that were about the size of my leg. Besides being physically tough, they were also mentally tough. The oldest son Hershie was in prison eventually because his dad had his mom down on the floor beating the crap out of her, and Hershie came up behind him with a hunting rifle, and shot him dead.

Howie was married at the time to a pretty girl, "Linda," that he usually neglected. I probably shouldn't have hung with Howie as it probably contributed to his eventual divorce. He was a lot of fun to hang with, and was the first person I ever met that called everyone "Dude". We had alcohol every hour of the day because Howie and I would go to a little store after closing on the canal. Howie could pound on the door and the proprietor came down before Howie woke up the neighborhood. Howie had him intimidated because he could go in and grab a case of beer any hour of the night, and away we went to drink. Howie always said "put it on my bill", and I don't think he ever paid it or even had a bill there.

I'VE GOT HIGH FRIENDS IN LOW PLACES

This was the beginning of the hippie times. I met a guy that was part of my first encounter with "Hippies". We were welcome at a place called "The Ranch" where about six or eight hippies lived. One was known as "Dirty Ned", and wasn't exactly clean, but I never found him to be too dirty either! He was only about seventeen at the time, but walked like an old man. He was raised near Seattle by rich parents and had done what they called - get high, tune in, and drop out! There were also two brothers there - Jon and Paul Sanyo. They, like everyone else there had long hair - I mean really long hair! We really didn't know what to think of Paul, but Jon was a fun loving, laughing sort of guy. He laughed at most everything. Allan Whiteman was a sort of studious type, who looked like he was from a farm. He always wore bib overalls and usually no shoes. He went outside even in the snow without shoes. I don't know how he did it. Skip was kinda the young buck of the place. It seemed like he had been taken under the other guy's wings. His outlook on life was great, and he said a lot of funny stuff.

Howie and I looked really out of place there as we were still short haired, fighting, drinking, car guys, with jobs. Few at the ranch had jobs, and were mostly listening to good music, and getting high. They put up with us, and maybe even liked us somewhat, and we liked a lot of the lifestyle at the ranch. We heard Grateful Dead, Quicksilver Messenger Service, Stones, Jimi Hendrix, over there for the first time. New incredible music to us. I started smoking pot again, and it all seemed to fit together really well.

Denny Kirby was a kind of a wise-ass guy we met along with a group of wild characters. He was probably the wildest and immediately reminded me of Eddie Haskel from "Leave it to Beaver" TV show. When he came into his folk's house where he lived, he either took a stack of dishes out of the cupboard, and threw them on the floor, or cut the goldfish in half with a pair of scissors. I asked him why? And he said "I just want my folks to know I've been home". His dad had heart trouble and Denny would even hide his heart pills, then startle his dad when he came around the corner. His folks were victims, when a guy called "Punkin Head" pushed a garden hose into Denny's bed early in the morning - and turned it on. He didn't know Denny and his folks had changed rooms since he'd been there last. Of course his folks got hosed and drenched and weren't at all happy!

Howie, Denny, someone I didn't know named Byron, and I took off to the ocean one Saturday in Denny's ride. It was kinda an odd group, because none of our personalities were alike; especially Howie and Dennys. All the way down there, Denny was needling Howie. Howie could wipe Denny out easily and Denny knew it, and just kept pushing. Byron and I were constantly keeping Howie from taking Denny out, and trying to get Eddie Haskel to shut up.

On the way back, Byron decided he was hungry, so we stopped at a McDonalds in Aberdeen. Pretty soon Howie is getting "Froggy" with a local. A fight breaks out, Byron and Denny flee to the car. Howie and I ended up backing out swinging on a bunch of locals that wanted a "go at it". We managed to punch our way to the car and we split. The locals jumped into their car and chased us about ten miles. That was the way it was if I hung with Howie. I never knew when he was going to start a beef, and I would have to defend myself.

On the way back we had Denny drop Howie and I off at my Uncle Red's where I left my car.

My Uncle Red was a real good guy, married to a very shy lady, who seldom said anything. They had one son Cousin Rod. I didn't see anyone of them much, as they lived across the bay, where I seldom went. Rod was a real pinball wizard during the time when pinball paid off cash. He was banned from many places in the county that had machines, because he always got them to pay off. Red was quite a fisherman which I wasn't. He made the best smoked salmon I have ever eaten, and always "layed" some on me when I came to visit.

After smoked salmon at Red's, Howie said "he knew of a party nearby". When we got there we were happy to see there were some ladies there. One in particular caught my eye. She was Pam - beautiful body, pretty, and clean cut. I immediately pounced on this one, because she was very easy to know. Her parents were very strict, and most of the time the only way I could see her was to go over to her house when she was babysitting her little brother. Made it real hard to get next to her. We went out on dates a few times, and she was fun. However on our last date, we were at a drive-in restaurant; waitress on skates and all. She got out and walked over to a Corvette convertible to talk to a guy she apparently knew. I walked over and was ignored. I could see she was hitting on him, and knew it was all over with her. She must have wanted to ride in the Corvette from now on.

I licked my wounds for a while but met a really good find. Karen was fair looking, good body with real big breasts, but what really attracted me to her was her great personality. She was the most fun chick, I had ever encountered. She had a lot of guy buddies, which some of whom were my buddies too. I moved about this time, to an old "alkie" named "Oil can Earl's" house. He lived in the big top floor, and rented the small lower floor apartment to a young expecting couple Mike and Beth. Mike worked in the Yard and was a sort of "average Joe" type. On the other hand Beth was a real beauty, a few months along. I ended up hanging with both some. I don't think Beth was quite ready for family life, but Mike was. I suspected she was maybe up to no good while Mike was on his swing shift working. I was right as they divorced eventually. "Oil Can Earl" drank wine constantly, and I sometimes drank with him. He let me live there for free, except sometimes his "battle ax" ex-wife would come by, and give me a load of crap about living there. I was cordial, but paid little attention to her. Karen spent time there, and had a good relationship with Earl. He actually was no problem, and let me party anytime.

I got put on swing shift - 4 to 12 a.m. I didn't like it because it put a serious damper on my dating and partying. I started getting in trouble for coming in buzzed, and it wasn't long before I got a D.U.I. I was downtown on my way to work, parking when a cop drove by real slow. He stopped, walked over to my car, and dragged me out. He said he could tell when he drove by me, I was drunk. He put me in the back and took me down to booking. After booking he started to take me downstairs to the jail, but I hauled off and popped him in the chops as hard as I could. After he came back up the stairs, he and a few cops knocked me down, and started dragging me down the stairs by my feet with my head bonking off the stairs all the way. I had the worst headache I had ever had when I woke up - what with my sore head and a bad hangover. When I went to court I was given thirty days, and could do it on weekends. I knew most all the guys in there because they were young hell raisers like me. A friend told me about some over the-counter stuff called Asmadore. It turned out it would make us really high because of an ingredient - Belladonna. I started taking some into jail on my weekends because the guards didn't check me well. We ate this stuff and got so high we were delirious. We made the best of the situation in jail, and had fun as much as possible. Since we were mostly friends it wasn't hard. There was a guy in there named Musky, who was a step brother of a couple of my friends. He thought he was cool, but most thought he was a joke. He ended up being the brunt of our jokes. Once when he was passed out on a rack at the jail, we lit his socks on fire while they were on him. Seemed like they just exploded. So the cops found out and decided to move Musky into his own trustee cell for his own good. Well when they brought the coffee with the meals in a big milk can, Musky got the left over coffee to put in his own coffee pot in his cell. He thought he was being smart by coming up to the little window in our main cell door, and proclaiming "I wish you could have some of this good coffee, but you common criminals can't have any". I never drank coffee so didn't care, but when we got the next milk can of coffee, the guys got their coffee, and we all pissed in the big milk can. Sure enough later on Musky came up to our little window with his cup of coffee saying "I wish you common criminals could have some of this coffee". We set about telling him "we don't want any because we pissed in it". I've never seen a man turn so green so suddenly. The cops heard us over the intercom, and one of the funnier cops came down saying "Hey Musky, I heard that coffee hit the spot". We got separated and thrown in solitary, but it was worth it, because we were getting out that evening anyway.

My friend Pete was in with us on one weekend. He was another "wise – ass" that got off doing bazaar things. The cops came in and told Pete he was to be the new trustee, as Musky had gotten out. A day later Pete was thrown back in with us. Seems they had Pete wash some of the patrol cars. He took the gas cap off of a couple of cars and filled them full of water. A while later the cops took off on a big 10-4, and got a couple blocks away when the cars died. They put two and two together, busted Pete and gave him thirty more days. Of course we all thought it hilarious, and he was a hero to us!

A jail friend of mine, Ted, seemed to almost always be in jail. I think he liked it or something because he even did time in prison eventually. On one occasion he stole a cop car and went joy riding until they boxed him in. We made the best out of jail by tying towels into a ball and shooting at a trash can. Ted and I were told we were going to be trustees. There was a little store across the street from the jail and we went over and bought candy, and snuck it in the jail with us. There was a nasty little

guy named Grass in jail with us. At night Ted and I were in one
cell together, and Grass was in the next alone. Grass started
sniveling about wanting candy, so we said "OK" and put M and
M's up my butt and farted them out then passed them over to
him at the front bars. He couldn't see what was going on, and
after a while Ted proclaimed "Grass, Grass ate candy out of
Joe's ass". We laughed so hard I thought we would blow an
Oring.

When I got through with this bunch of weekends, Karen
found out the Kinks were to play a concert on a revolving stage
in Seattle. Along with her friend and her boyfriend, we loaded
up in his car and went. The Kinks were "tight" and very good.
There was also the Turtles, and the Association on the show, but
we were really impressed with the Kinks. Karen liked them all.
I always thought concerts were well worth the money, and went
to all I could.

The next concert we went to see was The Yardbirds;
Crosby's first major band. Crosby would later be part of Crosby,
Stills, Nash, and Young. Crosby had on this big fur hat, and was
playing the song Turn, Turn, Turn, Turn. The Yardbirds had Jeff
Beck playing guitar for them, and the band very impressive.
The light show going on behind them on a big screen made the
show even better. This was the first light show we'd seen, but
since they were becoming all the rage, I saw many more. One
effect was made by showing projected light on the screen
through oil on water.

I came there with a guy we called "Billy Green Teeth",
an Indian guy with not so good teeth. He had an old Plymouth
Savoy. We had no money for gas or tickets so Billy suggested

we go up to a local gas station and till tap them. I went inside and got the kid to look under the hood while Billy slipped in and tapped the till for fifty bucks. It really was a dumb move, but it got us in the concert. It was a shaky proposition hanging with Billy. On another occasion we were cruising town early in the morning when Billy spotted a swab stumbling up an alley. He jumped out, went over to the guy and "cold conked" him. He was digging for the guy's wallet when I stopped him. It was a good thing I stopped him, as we got busted, but they let us go because there were no witnesses to back the swabs claim of assault. If Billy would have taken his wallet we would have gotten nailed for larceny. Billy was just too dangerous to my freedom, so I quit hanging with him. I don't know how with those green teeth, he was a chick magnet, but he was, and that was the biggest reason I hung with him in the first place.

Jon Cittio and I had a lot of fun messing around together, and he was a really funny guy. We'd go out drinking, and he liked to slip in some ones ride, pull the inside light bulb out so it couldn't come on, then shit on the driver's seat; and wipe his butt with whatever was available. Then we parked within eyeshot and drank and hoped someone would sit in the pile of poop. His plan was a good one, and sometimes someone either sat in the poop or put their hand in it. So he got the nickname of "Shittio". Now his sister was very short, not over four foot tall so she got the nickname Shorttio.

Their brother reportedly licked snot out of Dirty Ned's hand, so he got named "Snottio". So these siblings were known as "Shittio", "Shorttio", and "Snottio".

We finally smashed up my 56 Chev. We took off from a light and a small car pulled out from a side street and stopped. We "piled" right into the side of it. Fortunately no one was hurt, but I needed a ride, and settled on an "80 Suzuki" motor cycle. It was a bit small, but easy on gas and very maneuverable. Sometimes I rode up stairs to Charlotte's second story apartment. I rode the hell out of that bike, and even rode it to work with a flat back tire for about two weeks.

There was a lot of pot around and we smoked plenty. I started painting the Zig Zag guy on the papers, onto my boots, my "80 Suzuki" and a couple of other things. I was starting to want to look a little more "hippy like". You know when you smoke a lot of pot it makes your hair grow longer. So then my buddy Jim started calling me Mr. Zig Zag, and it seemed to stick with some of my other friends as well.

Pizza was starting to be a big hit, and pizza places sprang up everywhere. There was one particular place downtown, where everybody "cool" ended up. I went down to this place called "Pizza Pete's", with my new acquaintance Jake, A.K.A. "Jake the Nut". At first I didn't know what the name was about, but I found out. When we went inside, it was pretty full of people we both knew. Pretty soon after we sat down we heard everyone kinda chanting, "hang a nut", "hang a nut - hang a nut". It got louder and louder and soon Jake stood up, unzipped his zipper, and hung his giant nut on a pizza platter, he took from a startled waitress. The whole place just erupted. Seems Jake had something wrong with one of his nuts, and it was the size of a softball. The whole thing was quite impressive. I ended up enjoying many wild times with Jake.

We ended up a few nights later going to a party at

Charlotte's house. She had some other chick living with her, and Denny Kirby, Duane Gobles, Dick Rome, and my good bud - Homo were there. Jake was also a phantom shitter, as in Charlotte's apartment. He crapped everywhere he could, in her shoes in the bedroom, in the bathtub, where he used the shower curtain to wipe. For his crowning achievement he laid a turd like a banana across the top of a bowl of fruit. That night there was also a cop there out of uniform. We didn't know it at first, until Denny Kirby, remembered who he was. Duane called him on it, and the guy tried to punch him. Duane proceeded to punch him twice in the face, bulged his eye out, and knocked him out. The next day we were cruising town, and this cop was standing in the middle of the intersection directing traffic, with a big shiner. We drove by him real slow, rolled down our windows and verbally abused the guy, all the time laughing and pointing at him. It's real rare when we got a chance to ridicule a cop, and we liked it.

My friend Pete was going to get married, and there would be a big party somewhere. Pete's girl was alright, and I thought my friend was doing o.k. for himself. My friend Casteel and I went out to his reception in my new car, a pretty 59 Chev Impala hardtop. We both got pretty hammered, and on the way out there I had to take a wiz and pulled over to the side of the little used highway. I was standing at the top of a tall bank over a gully full of blackberry brambles. As I'm standing there doing my thing, I fell forward, rolled down the hill into brambles covered in wiz. It hurt and I stunk. Casteel wouldn't help me out at all, but I managed to crawl out. We loaded up, and headed the rest of the way to Pete's reception. You can imagine what a hit I was all scratched up and bloody, smelling like piss, and staggering. Well,

I was picking fights with guys, so the crowd dragged me out to my car, loaded me up and off I went. I was way too intoxicated to be behind the wheel. It really proved itself out, because I missed a bridge over a creek and stuck my 59 Chev into the mud twenty feet below. Next thing I woke up in the hospital struggling to breath. Seems I had drove a rib through my lung, on impact with the dash. After I thought I would suffocate, they gave me oxygen. The doctor pushed my broken rib around with his palm, and after a day or so my lung seemed to pump back up to normal. The state patrol came into my room, and tried to get me to "fess-up" and admit I was driving. I landed in the mud, and they couldn't prove I was driving because I wasn't in the car when they got there. I used the "mercy card", and said "I couldn't answer questions because I couldn't breathe". The excuse got rid of them anyway. I don't know what happened to Casteel from the party on. The last thing I remembered about the night of the wreck was hearing the Stones "Get off of my Cloud", blaring on the radio. Now my wheels were totaled, and I was busted up!

During my healing Denny came by and got me, and we went over to pick up a couple of other guys. My hippy buddies from the "Ranch", had gotten another place near town they called "the shop", because it was right below a guy's auto repair shop. We always had fun with these guys, and today would be no different. I had an old transformer that was about the size of a loaf of bread. We put a cord on it and a couple of bare wires going straight up. When it was plugged into electricity it would arc across a "Jacob's Ladder", all the way to the top. Dirty Ned decided he would stick his tongue between it. It knocked him against the wall, and his tongue had a little hole through it, with smoke coming out. We all got a good laugh. Then we smoked another joint, and decided to head out to the canal to a girl who wanted us to party with her. Besides Dirty Ned, Duane, Homo and myself there was Jon. We decided to go by way of the old highway. About halfway out, we came to a flashing lights scene, where the cops had everyone stopped. Seems a motorcycle and car had a collision and the murder cycle lost, and the rider was dead. While we were sitting there waiting, Denny looks out at the dark ground: "hey you guys, there's something on the ground below me". He got out and got back in with it. It was a severed human arm!

The next time I came over to the "shop", it was snowing, and when we looked out later, it had accumulated about a foot. Alan Whiteman decided to walk downtown with us, but he wore no shoes, as he never wore shoes. I couldn't believe anyone could stand to walk around barefooted in the snow for an hour. We found a Coca-Cola sign built like a big bottle cap on the side of a store and ripped it off and began riding it. It didn't snow very often, but we made the best of it when it did. During that time it seemed like everyone was trying to do something more outlandish than the next guys.

Now I needed another new ride, and Walt the mechanic above the "shop" sold me a 37 Chev coupe, with a bullet hole in the trunk. It was supposed to have been used in an armed robbery, and had been shot at in the getaway. It made a good story anyway. I got a 283 Chev V-8 from a friend with four speed, and put it in the 37 Chev. I couldn't believe how well it went in, and had it running strong in no time. The brakes and electrical weren't very good, but it sure ran strong. Women liked riding in this car also. We were using it to take me and my buds down to Shelton to work dragging Christmas trees out of the woods for loading. The only thing good about "dragging" was it was a job, and it was out in the woods.

Homo, and a guy named "Redding" and I went together. We rode in trucks out to the woods, in the middle of nowhere. Sometimes we stumbled onto rabbits, deer, cougar, bobcats, or black bears. Homo and I always wore full raingear because we almost always partied all night, and were so tired we laid down in the brush and slept instead of dragging. On one occasion they couldn't find us and we woke up to find we had been left behind. That was the end of that job. It was a long hike and hitch-hike to get out of there when we were left behind. They fired us when we came back for our final check.

When I was working at the car wash the following spring, I ran into a nice girl who I eventually dated. Alice was married at the time to the owner of the car wash's son. We didn't make much money at the place, so it was common for us to just suck any change up in the vacuum, then get the money out later. Another girl there pointed out a creepy looking guy standing across the street, and claimed he was stalking her. I went over and asked him "what's your problem dude". It turned into a scuffle and he went to punch me, but I dodged him easily. He had some goggles on his forehead, as he had arrived on a little mickey-mouse scooter. I pulled on his goggles and let them go and they hit him in his eyes so hard, they blacked both eyes. It turned out to be a good move, because the girl I was defending, was a cop's daughter - a celebrity cop. His name was Ralph, and he tried to terrorize the kids cruising town. The saying was "checked by Ralph", some guys even had bumper stickers with those words. The cops didn't do anything about blacking the "creep's" eyes, and Ralph looked on me favorably. Down the road, he let me slide a few times.

I was living with a new bud named Dave, whom they called "creature". Dave had an old Studebaker at his mom's house we called the "Bat Mobile" as it was black, and very odd looking. We came around the corner across from Dave's mom's house on two wheels one early morning, and Ralph the cop was right there. Of course he pulled us over, and read us the riot act. This was the first time Ralph let me slide.

I did go to court the next day for a drinking and fighting arrest. There was a guy in the back of the court called "Treptoes". He wore all black including a black leather coat, kinda an unkempt greasy looking guy, whose presence wasn't lost on anyone. He walked with a swagger that said "I'm tough and don't mess with me"! I ended up spending time in jail with him, and we became good friends, and I partied with him occasionally. He was found dead at a friend's apartment years later by Howard Green. When Howard found him he had to go get someone else to come over and call 911. Howard couldn't because he had a warrant out for him at the time, so he had to take off before the cops arrived. I'm sure the warrant was for fighting as that was what Howard was about. "Treptoes" could be funny, like showing up at a rock festival called the "Buffalo Party Convention" with a cardboard sleeping bag, off of a long mirror, as he had no real sleeping bag. He was always a little dangerous, and I always stayed aware of that. He "shot up" drugs sometimes including heroine, and that led to his demise. We didn't have a lot in common because I never "shot" anything up, but I liked him anyhow.

My 37 Chev ended up being more work than I wanted, so I traded it to my buddy Mike that used to live below me at "Oil Can Earls". He had a 55 Chev hardtop and after we swapped motors, he had the 37 and I had the 55 hardtop. He ended up really fixing up the 37 coupe and dragging it. I was happy to have a ride that didn't require so much work and maintenance.

Friday night Homo came by and picked me up. He already had Karen and a couple of other girls I didn't know with him. We met up with a bunch of other people, and decided to have a "keg party" in the woods. Word gets around quick and we ended up going through the keg pretty fast. Homo, Karen, Homo's "squeeze" and I went to get another. Somehow I ended up staggering drunk, walking across the highway with an empty keg on my shoulder. A car came along and hit me head on.

My mom was told by the coroner, when she showed on the scene, that I had been decapitated. There was so much blood he couldn't tell for sure. I was immediately shipped off to the hospital.

CHAPTER 9

PSYCHEDELIC

My so called friends that were with me all shot off their mouths to investigators. Instead of using common sense and not say anything, they just kept talking. Like one of my brothers says "common sense isn't so common". He got that right! My mom was a wreck, and almost got in a wreck in the cab, on the way to the hospital. I can imagine after she had been told "I was decapitated"!

I lived through it, but had serious damage to me. I had to have over 500 stitches in my head, as when I was hit the bumper and hood hit me, threw me in the air, and my head went through the windshield and back out. My head got most of the damage from coming back through the windshield. I also had a broken leg and hip. I was fortunate my long-time doctor was great at stitching. Except for scars around my eyes, I really didn't look bad.

I spent about two months in the hospital recovering. When I went back to work I limped pretty bad, and the boss put me through a walking test, that I passed. It was all downhill from there, as I was still getting drunk and partying. One particular time I came in loose, and was working on the t-beams on a deck section laid upside down on the slab. My job was to weld the t-beams to the steel deck plate. I was so drunk and hung-over, I laid down between the beams and started welding. Soon I passed out and my rod stuck; turned red hot, and started my leathers on fire. Another worker saw me, got a fire extinguisher, and put me out. That among other things didn't endear me to the Yard, and was told I would be fired in a couple of weeks, but that I could quit before then and it would look better for me. I really never liked working there, and decided to just let them fire me. They were happy to get rid of me, and I never wanted to work there again. My dad was a big shot there, and he thought my firing was the end of the world. It turned out to be a good decision later on, because a year or two later, I was drawing unemployment and wanted to take the summer off. The Employment Dept. decided to send me down to the Yard to work for a contractor. I could not go on the base again, because was fired - so I was able to take the summer off.

        Besides losing a couple of months of my life in pain, losing my job, and having to pay my own hospital bills, they wanted me to pay for the damage done to his car. I had taken out his bumper, grill, hood, and windshield. Because my socalled friends had told them I was walking across the highway, not in a crosswalk, and had an empty keg on my shoulder, drunk; they found me at fault. I refused to pay for his car anyway.   My welding experience served me well because I was able to get a job in Tacoma at a place called Tides Air. We were building electrical parts for a dam. Dams produce so much power they use aluminum plates, connected together by copper plates, to handle all that electricity. They heated the copper plates up red hot and my job was to weld them with a wire feed welder. It was so hot I had to wear an asbestos suit. It was an easy going job, except I was swing shift, and it cut into my party life considerably. I made a deal with another worker, whereby we would swap clocking each other out. We didn't get greedy, and only did it once in a while - so jumping the fence and leaving

halfway through the shift worked until the job was over.
One of the perks of working there, was meeting a black guy
named Sylvester, who was a singer in a rock roll band. He hung
with me because I knew a lot of chicks, and ended up hanging
with him because I went to his gigs, and a lot of parties
afterward. He was a nice enough guy and we did a lot of
partying together. One thing I was aware of was when Sly was
with me, we were in sync; when we got together with other
blacks, Sly would ignore me, like he didn't know me. This
wouldn't be the last time I witnessed this behavior among my
black friends.

 One Friday when I jumped the fence, I went back to
Bennington to party with a buddy called Ron Swab. We left my
car and jumped into his 53 Chev. He knew of a party and we
headed out. Ron was a good looking guy with a mole on his
cheek that was a plus for him. He had five brothers who were all
"cool". I ended up hanging with all of them, one time or
another. This particular night we found a couple of parties
which were out of town to the west, toward the canal. They were
both light on the women, and we decided to leave. Ron was real
drunk and wanted me to drive. I was only sort of drunk! We
went over the Little Beef Bridge where I had crashed my 59
Chev into the mud a year earlier. We were headed toward the
Big Beef Bridge, and must have been traveling way to fast,
because we rolled and ended up upside down on top of the
bridge. I ended up on my back on the inside of the top of the car,
and Ron was hanging upside down still strapped in. The engine
was on fire, still running upside down, and fuel on fire, was
pouring out of the carburetor. There was also a big puddle

of gas spreading from the gas tank. Ron says "what do we do now? I reached over and unfastened the belt, and Ron fell in a pile on the inside of the roof. We got out, and a passerby put out the fire with an extinguisher. Neither one of us got hurt, except for the usual lumps and bruises. I had crashed a car on both the Big and Little Beef Bridges! We were able to get out of there without getting busted, but felt some responsibility for the crash so I helped Ron get and put a 51 Chev Panel Delivery together. We had to change the motor, transmission and other parts, but it ended up being a "cool" ride. Fortunately Ron didn't get "pissed"; we remained friends, and hung out in that "cool" panel.

Homo wanted to get a place, so we got an apartment in Silverville. It was real nice - too nice for us. The first night, Dirty Ned, Allan Whiteman, Skip, Duane, Karen, and a crew too numerous to name, showed up for a party with Homo and I. We were all very much into red wine now, and because this place had white rug, it was a disaster. That wine stained the rug pretty bad. The manager came down to see what the commotion was about; saw the stained rug, and promptly threw us out. We hadn't even moved any furniture in; hadn't even spent a night there; and we were already evicted. It might have been some type of record - at least among my friends and me. We still needed a pad and decided on an apartment in a U-shaped complex in the other end of town. It was small, and not at all nice, but it suited us fine. Homo was working somewhere, and my job at Tides Air hadn't run out yet.

I had blown the motor in my 55 Chev and was looking for a good ride. Duane had a very unique car he sold me. It was a 51 Chev that had been a high school driver's ed. Car. It had two steering wheels, brake pedals, gas, and clutch pedals. It was made that way so the teacher could control the car from the passenger seat. Sometimes when we cruised town, I climbed out the driver's side window and stood on the running board while we were moving. Of course Homo or Duane or whoever was in the passenger seat was driving. I hammed it up by gyrating around, kicking out a leg or something just to be funny. We had to be very careful when we did it, because even Ralph the cop would have locked me up and thrown away the key if he caught me.

One evening at the apartment, Homo showed up with a few guys and wanted to go party. I had the only wheels there because I had blown the motor in Homo's 57 Chev hardtop a couple of weeks before. Besides Homo, the other guys were Marvin Davies, Billy K, and Vince, new acquaintances. Marvin was a kind of wise-ass who almost always wore a sport coat, and was a big blues guy. Billy K. was a very popular guy; very funny, who also really followed the blues music. Vince was easy going, and soft spoken. I was sick that night and after listening to B.B. and Albert King for a while, decided I wasn't up to going with them. They wanted to use my 51 Chevy, so I let them. After they left I was cruising on the couch when the D.J. on the radio said "Bobby Kennedy had been assassinated". What a sad event and I have to admit to tearing up when it sank in. Just after midnight the guys walked in and told me they were stumping my car at the dump; it started running rough, so they burned it! I was sick and really didn't care. The ride was fun while it lasted.

A couple of nights later, we could hear a scratching on our door. Homo opened the door and there was a huge St.

Bernard dog standing there, who promptly walked in. We gave him a bunch of hot dogs, and he laid down, went to sleep after his meal. I think he had some kind of dreams about chasing rabbits. He would run, laying there while sleeping. He came over most nights, and we kinda felt like he was our dog.

Billy K. was living with his wife in one of the other apartments a couple over from us. His marriage was over and he had to move out. He didn't have his last month's rent, and decided to pass all his stuff out the back window so the manager wouldn't know he was leaving. It was a good plan except about half way through the move, he passed something out the window, and the manager was standing there to take it. "What's going on Bill"?

It was getting toward summer and we all decided to camp together on a hill overlooking the city dump. We had all lost our jobs, and didn't have any money to get a place anyway. Billy K. came up with a big squad tent somewhere. We set it up on a hill with a steep dirt road going up to it. We thought the cops couldn't drive up the hill, and wouldn't walk all the way up the hill to get to us. The place had a great view of Seattle about thirty miles away. We were into loganberry wine, and busted the limbs on a madrona tree, and put logy bottles on it. It soon looked pretty decorated. The side toward the dump had a big cliff; we lit couches on fire, and threw them off the cliff when we were bored. A lot of friends from town came out, and we partied the hell out of the place. It lasted about a month, until to our surprise a couple of cops drove their "Pork Chop" up there, and showed up in our tent door. We weren't supposed to camp there, and they "rousted" us out of there.

Now I had no job, no car, and nowhere to live. I got a job at a car dealership downtown. It was a Ford dealership, and they sensed I liked Chevys. I managed to stick to this job for a few months, and paid off a "cool" 50 Dodge wrap around window truck. It ran o.k. but was very good looking, and rare. I also came up with a place on Broad Street. This house was owned by an old couple, was very cheap, and suited me fine. They left a big organ there, and it was fun working at playing it. I met a neighbor guy who could really play organ well, and was starting to play harps. We did some real good "jamming" together. We were both into blues, and blues seemed pretty easy to play.

I got a dog also called "Louie the Licker". If someone passed out on my couch, they got licked by this huge German shepherd, until they woke up sticky. He also didn't like redheaded people, or people in uniforms. One evening the door flew open, a red-headed friend Donny ran in, slammed the door just in time to keep Louie from biting him. Donny stated "that was close". Pete and I later down the road, were driving into a State Park; Louie was in the back of my van out of sight, and about the time the Ranger in uniform, got to my driver's window, Louie shot his head out at him barking and snarling. It startled the Ranger so bad he fell down, and told us to "leave because we couldn't bring that dog in there".

I got an offer on my 50 Dodge truck I couldn't refuse, and traded it for an old 49 Plymouth Sedan with "suicide doors", and a bunch of cash. They called the rear doors "suicide doors" because they opened forward. We got going fast and someone threw the back doors open, and they would dribble off the side.

Real fun, except they got hard to close at all, so we had to body slam into them to get them to close. Eventually one completely flew off. The front bearings got dry and wobbly, and not wanting to do any wrenching on it, it just got worse. We turned a corner in town at one of the busiest intersections; halfway through the corner the whole wheel fell off, and the car dove "clunk" into the pavement. My car had part of the intersection blocked, and wasn't going to move on its own. We told everyone honking we were going to get help, and took off, never to return. The car wasn't yet in my name so it worked very well. We never heard another thing about it and that was the end of the road for that car.

Howard had a bunch of brothers, and I started chumming around with Lanny Green, one of the brothers. Lanny, Orville, Jim, and a couple of girls and I were out on the Canal partying until early in the morning. Lanny had borrowed the car from his brother Aaron. Aaron was probably the toughest of the Green brothers. He was legendary for his fighting ability. Anyway Lanny, Orville, Jim, the two girls and I were going down a mostly deserted highway to another party. I was in the back with Jim and one of the girls, when Lanny passed a car at 50 m.p.h on a corner. Next I am laying in the woods with blood trickling out of my chin, and Lanny kicking my side asking "are you all right"? It seems Lanny had passed head on into another car? I flew through the windshield mostly unscathed, but Jim wasn't so lucky and his injuries proved fatal. The others in the car got varying injuries. Later I had to go with Lanny to his brother, Aaron's house and tell him we totaled the car. Jim was still alive at that point, but Jim had broken his neck fatally. Besides being very sad, I was really scared of facing Aaron. He took it better than I thought he would, and he just slapped Lanny around some - probably because he was sad about Jim. I figured at that point, if I didn't change my ways I might be next to die. I had been in so many car wrecks, and couldn't keep it up. I made an effort from then on to keep myself, alcohol, and cars away from each other.

Jan worked for a guy name Harold building homes. Harold was a real Christian and probably wouldn't have hired me except for Jan. Jan was a great carpenter and worked with another carpenter George, and I was the laborer. There was usually only us as Harold was usually busy taking care of business.

George was a funny guy that always called people "rat finks". He always wore overalls and on one job we didn't have any bathroom, so we had to go out to the woods to do our thing. George went out to the woods to crap, and when he came out and flipped his straps over his shoulder, the shit flew, as he had crapped on his straps. We got a good laugh and George went home to change.

My brother Jan, being the joker he always was, always used me for the brunt of his tricks. I smoked those little cigars for a time, and Jan put finish nails in them when I wasn't looking. This made them smoke real hot. Sometimes I fell asleep at lunch time, and Jan would staple me or nail me to the floor. Even though I was the brunt of Jan's jokes, I really enjoyed working with Jan and George. One morning when I got out of my car, a couple of beer cans fell out, and rolled down the driveway. Harold fired me right there.

My newest car was a 59 Chev 4 door wagon. It looked rough, ran rough, but it always ran. The rear floor was completely rotted out, and I had a chunk of plywood over it. It also had charging problems, so I kept a broom handle inside, and when it quit charging I could smack the wall at the front of the motor and it started charging. The hole in the floor was handy because we shoved all our beer cans out of it.

I had met a girl named Litia; a very pretty girl, but also very young. We were up visiting her Aunt and Uncle when we mentioned I needed a place. Jean told me a guy they rented from had a big old house up the road toward the dump we had camped at earlier. I went up to look at it. It was three story with an unfinished basement. It had four bedrooms, and was really out of the way on five acres. There was electricity, running water, but no inside toilet. It had an outhouse. The house was an old homestead, and was built shortly after the turn of the century. We found the owner, and he agreed to rent it to me for an incredible $25 a month. Homo was going to move in, but never did. Bill, Marvin, a couple of southern guys, one we just called "South", and I moved in right away. Others including a guy we called Barry Gutler, moved in also. Soon it was one big "crash pad", with a party going on constantly. After a while the outhouse got so full of crap, there was a little mountain of crap sticking up above the seat. One of the wood walls inside the house was getting wiped out, because the southern guys were fond of knife throwing. There were two guys that just drove in to stay for a few days at a time.

One of them was Daviduke, who worked as a carny. He was out with the circus for a few weeks, then returned with lots of pot. He liked "Cream" a lot and we were playing them a lot, along with Rod Stewart's "Superstition", Canned Heat, Alvin

Lee, Joe Cocker, Paul Butterfield, and the Who were always playing among many others.

Another guy that visited was Tom, a drug dealer with a VW Bus he called the "Magic Bus" after the Who song. He always had pot, and felt compelled to lay drugs on us for letting him camp in the yard in his bus. He rolled in with some exotic L.S.D. like "orange Wedge", "Blue Barrells", or "Window Paine". Occasionally I did some and "Orange Wedge" seemed to be the most potent. Everything moved including the road and ground that seemed to roll like waves. Sometimes we had flashbacks. I saw something outlandish, then when I looked again, it would be gone. It was fun to take L.S.D. with other people, because we usually saw something different, but sometimes we all saw the same thing, like the car ferry flying in the air. When L.S.D. first came out, there were dealers selling it right in front of cops, because there wasn't yet a law against it. A regular at our house Ray, seemed to be always high on it. That was scary, as he had a 16 gauge shotgun, and hunted pheasant in our front acres. I think he put buckshot in the neighbor's house at least once. Once Ray had shot a pheasant, and as we were frying it in a pan on the stove, a couple of Sheriffs' Deputies showed up. We told them we didn't know what they were talking about. That didn't fly, because there were feathers from cleaning all over the ground in front of the door. This same scenario would play out in Alaska, except with a stolen chicken, a year or so later.

A couple of people brought a girl out one day that was "trippin" on L.S.D. This girl was so high she took all her clothes off and ran around the yard incoherently. It was quite a show, and soon people were all over, even on our roof watching her

because she looked good as a pretty, naked, wild girl would.
We had a phone and some furniture in our main room that had
gone through a fire. The phone was half melted and the furniture
all bubbled. The walls were all painted by anyone who wanted
to paint their trip in florescent paint. The whole scene was
psychedelic and perfect for acid. You know we had a black light
that made the florescent paint glow.

Litia came up and hung with me, but she wasn't very
sharp, and was the brunt of my friend's jokes. They mostly
called her "The Genius". She had her own drugs, mainly speed
and downers. Occasionally she dropped acid with me, and we'd
have a weird, but good time. She had some great looking
girlfriends that had good personalities, and were a real plus when
they were there. Karen was a real pretty blond that hung with us
a lot.

Tom wanted to take us to a concert, and he took myself,
Bill, Litia, Karen, and Diane in his "Magic Bus". The concert
was Arthur Brown and Focus in Seattle. Of course we drank and
Tom was holding PCP so we smoked some. PCP is horse or
elephant tranquilizer and is usually dropped on mint leaves, and
rolled and smoked. We were really buzzing when we went in
and it was a perfect concert for it. Arthur Brown was very exotic
and played keyboard, along with a base, and drummer. His set
was kind of like a musical, and all led up to his hit "Fire". He
came back out to do "Fire" with his head on fire, and his legs
going like they were made of rubber. Then Focus came on and
did a good set that ended with their hit "Hocus Pocus". The
keyboard player was the guy that sang the high parts, and he
sang so high pitched, if there were any glass in the place, it

would have shattered. We were totally wet and exhausted when
it was over and returned home satisfied and "burned out".
I was due to go to court the next day. Litia, Karen, Diane, and I,
were stopped in my car for drinking Ripple Wine a week earlier,
and because they were minors, I got nailed for contributing to
minors. My lawyer was Fred Cahill, and I needed to be
represented on this one. I didn't know it at the time but the
headlines in the local newspaper would later read
"LOCAL LAWYER CAHILL MURDERED IN HIS OWN
DRIVEWAY"!

CHAPTER 10

SKYRIVER

There was talk that there was to be a "Rock Festival" in Sultan, Washington soon. "Rock Festival" was a term I had not heard before, but it was said to be outdoors, for days with day and night music from national and local bands. Ray and I "hitched" up there with just sleeping bags on our shoulder, and a couple of bucks in our pockets. It was to be the "SkyRiver Rock Festival and Lighter than Air Fair". It was close to the Skykomish River and had a Hot Air Balloon on a long tether, and could be raised and lowered for an incredible view of the place.

It was in the first part of the summer, but because it was in the Cascade Mountain Foothills, the weather was a little wet. But like they say about Washingtonians "They don't tan, they rust", so the weather was no big deal, as it was warm. The Festival was off a side road, and the State Patrol tried to stop it at first, but when they just got overwhelmed by thousands of people, they reverted to just traffic control. People were doing drugs, drinking, and thoroughly enjoying themselves. There were people going up in the Hot Air Balloon, and everything seemed to be free, including the people there.

The first music I heard was Van Morrison singing "Brown Eyed Girl", then "Moondance" after that. There were no cops inside, and everyone seemed to be doing just fine. I

thought I could sell some "Lids" there, and immediately thought
of Tom. I worked my way back down to Sultan, and called Tom
and told him to bring a few kilos to the festival. He agreed and
in a few hours he showed at the festival in the "Magic Bus". I
had an old detective-looking brim hat on and put a little sign that
read "Lids" on each side of the hat. He provided me with ounce
"lids" and we agreed I would make five dollars on each one sold.
I ended up selling almost one hundred "lids" there. It was a
great way to mingle. Most everyone wanted to talk to me, and
sometimes I did some swapping for what was needed. People
were sliding down a muddy hill, sometimes naked, into a muddy
pond at the bottom. I watched that a lot, because I thought the
muddy, naked women looked great and evidently many people
agreed because there was a huge crowd of spectators.

That night Big Mama Thornton and the Chambers
Brothers came on the stage. I walked by the side of the stage and
noticed my friend Allan drinking out of a bottle with the "Big
Mama". Her blues were great and got me all fired up for the
next band. Between the bands was a black comedian who I
hadn't seen before, but he was one of the funniest guys I had
ever seen. I heard his name was Richard Pryor! The next band
that came on was all black except for a white drummer. They
played a few songs that sounded like a cross between gospel and
rock music. This was the Camber's Brothers and their last song
was "Time Has Come Today", all twenty, twenty five minutes of
it, and they "tore the place up"! The next few days featured
bands like The Grateful Dead, Jesse Collin Young, and some
great local Seattle bands like the Daily Flash.

My buddy Allan was so drunk during the Grateful Dead,
he had passed out in a ditch full of water with his head resting

out of the water. A little dog came along, lifted his leg, and pissed on Allan's head. All he could do was swat at the dog and continue to lay there. It was hilarious.

The last major band to perform was Santana. I was really pumped over this music. I couldn't believe how well Carlos, Greg Rolley, and the others played "Soul Survivor". That place was "rockin", and no one was sitting down - everyone was "rockin". Seemed everyone from Bennington was there. I had witnessed free everything, including free love, great people, music, and the most fun, I had ever had to that point, but it was over to soon. Ray disappeared, and I caught a ride back with Tom, with almost five hundred dollars in my pocket made from selling "lids". I liked Tom's VW Bus and when I got back I bought one from Parker, which had the front smashed in. I used it for about a month, figured out it was a piece of crap, so I sold it when the clutch cable broke, for about what I paid. I went back to the old reliable 59 Chev wagon with the hole in the floor.

Turned out my lawyer Fred Cahill was shot with a shotgun, in his drive way, after work, by an unknown assailant. My mom told me he tried to put the bite on her, and he was a known "womanizer". I figured he had defended a woman, and got to close, and the husband did him in. He lived in a house on a high bank above the salt water. Since it was downtown, the assailant probably escaped by the beach. I went down to that beach and looked through the undergrowth for the shotgun and couldn't find it. I also waded in the water at low tide, to see if it was thrown in. Since the local cops said "they had no clues", I thought it would be "cool" to find the gun. Fred used to intimidate police on the stand, and I don't think he was popular with them. That might explain why I don't think the crime was ever solved. Maybe the cops didn't try very hard. My court date was delayed due to Fred's death, so I set about finding another lawyer. My buds were all talking about a lawyer named Bill Faser. When I met him, he seemed very smart, young, a little arrogant, and he maybe smoked a little dew. We went to court, and somehow he got everything thrown out. He seemed to be just as advertised.

Before my case was heard, a guy's case came up, where he had tried to out run the law in his car. The judge was an old guy named Lewis. The arresting cop got up on the stand and gave his account of the chase. He said the "perp had raced through town at a high rate of speed, running stop signs and red lights and almost ran over an old lady at an intersection". People and dogs were running for their lives. When the Judge asked the offender what had happened, the guy stated "his gas pedal stuck". Judge Lewis just lifted his glasses and said "do you expect me to believe that"? Because the guy amused the judge, he let him off really easy.

Karen and Diane had a problem of their own then. Za Za Gabor came to town, to Penney's, to push some beauty product at a public appearance. Karen and Diane heard about it, put on some holy jeans with no underwear on. They were two knockout blonds, and with skin showing they headed down to Penney's. They were both drunk and really "yucking it up". They stood in the front of the crowd ridiculing Gabor, and when the cops came and told them to "shut up, and go home and put some decent clothes on", they just got louder. Typical bazaar behavior I would expect from them, so I went to the jail to bail them out. The cops said "they were drunk and couldn't be released until that evening; so I returned then. I paid their bail for a "drunk in public" charge.

In another incident involving those two, Karen lived at home and her folks had left town for a few days. We decided to have a party there. Of course word got out fast, and soon the house was full of drunk, rowdy people. After a few hours of this, the neighbors called the cops. Her house had tile roofs, and there was a little enclosed deck above the front door. When the cops came Karen and Ray started pulling tiles off the roof and throwing them down on the cops below. Then the cops got serious and came in force. I managed to grab Karen, Diane, and another couple of chicks, and head out the back door. Just in time, because the area soon became saturated with cops; but we had escaped. We all went to my house until it all blew over. Only Ray and one other got arrested.

Next day Bill, Daviduke, and a guy called "Durpee", just because the name seemed to fit so good; Barry Gutler, and I went down to Barrys sister's house. The neighborhood didn't have much parking so we kinda had to double-park. Soon as we got in Marsha's house, Daviduke pulled out a lid, and started rolling. We all smoked our "brains out", and then there was a knock at the door. Bill opened the door and closed it, and in a dull voice said "the cops are outside". No one took him seriously, since he didn't seem alarmed, but then we heard some more knocking at the door. This time Marsha answered it, swung it wide open, and we could see two cops standing there. She said "the cops <u>are</u> here", then slammed the door in their face again. By now we're all bumping into each other wondering what to do. No one bothered to pick up the "lid" and papers that were in plain sight on the coffee table. Then there was a knock again, and Marsha put on her best face and opened the door. This time one of the cops said "we had to move our double parked car". Marsha sad "OK officer" and that was that. The cops could easily see the "lid", and papers on the table, and hadn't done anything about it. Being a house full of notorious characters, we could hardly believe the "non-bust". My house on Warner was starting to draw a lot of attention from the cops, and was getting "Hot". The cops were even sending "Rats" to our house to set us up, but we knew who the "Rats" were, and lumped them up, and sent them on their way. People weren't coming over as much, because they knew we were "hot". Even the southern guys went back to Greenback, Tennessee.

Litia informed me she had a "bun in the oven", and her parents wanted to talk to me. She was seventeen at the time and her folks wanted me to marry her, or I'd be in trouble. Though I didn't love Litia, I relished the idea of having a son - I hoped. So we got hitched in a little ceremony. We moved out of Warner house", and got our own little place. I put a stop to the drugs for both of us during the pregnancy. Our first house was a little place right down the road from where I grew up. We had the upstairs pad, while an acquaintance Ken and his new wife lived downstairs. I was doing my best to stay away from my old buddies as much as possible to give my marriage and future fatherhood a chance. I got a little more serious about working and got jobs as a laborer through the union. That only lasted a short time, then I went to work at a local Naval Base, loading bombs on ships bound for Viet Nam.

CHAPTER 11

BOMBS AWAY

This ended up being one of the best jobs I ever had. I was working with guys my own age and knew most of them, plus was well paid. We loaded bombs that came in on trains, onto Liberty Class freighters bound for Viet Nam. We usually worked what we called "seven tens". Seven days of ten hours straight, then three days off. We worked 2 p.m. to 12 a.m. At the end of the ten days we all had good-sized checks waiting for us. A local tavern cashed every ones checks when we got off. Sometimes we loaded up and headed off to Wallace Idaho; that was known for its whore houses, or maybe Vancouver Canada; that was known for everything, or some other destination. Usually we got pretty drunk and raised hell all the way. A bunch of us got in a beef at a restaurant about halfway to Vancouver. It seemed Roy didn't like his steak, so he rubbed it all over a window. The chef was a little guy. He was wearing his tall white chef's hat and Roy pushed it down over his face, and the battle was on. We managed to escape without going to jail. That was a pretty funny move on Roy's part, as the hat got stuck when Roy pulled it down.

Sometimes ships already had huge boxes of hard liquor in the holds when they arrived. We would take a knife and cut into the big cardboard cases, and pull bottles of hard liquor out. Those bottles were stashed and ended up in our cars in the parking lot. They wouldn't let us drive to the pier, so we parked in a lot near the fence, and rode a bus down to the pier. My buddy Pete and I, Homo, and Racoombs rode together to work.

Pete and I deliberately ate chili and hardboiled eggs before we left. That gave us some overwhelming stinky farts, and we got our jollies by cutting loose at work. The bus driver stopped the bus once, and everyone got out because the stench was so bad. Or else I walked up to a few guys talking, and cut a "silent but deadly" one and walk away a ways, and watch them blame each other. It's amazing what an idle mind will come up with.

Pete was a funny guy, just married to a pretty little thing. They rented a small house in the middle of town. We both liked to work on cars, and spent time rebuilding Chevy V-8 engines. We raised a lot of hell together, on and off work, and I was surprised his wife put up with us.

Tinker was kind of a weenie looking guy, and was always talking about how great he was at Karate. Pete took a piece of 2x4 and sawed most of the way through the back, and laid it on the edge of the dumpster. He yelled "Hey Tinker, watch this". He proceeded to karate chop it, and it fell into the dumpster in pieces. Tinker decided he wanted to show off, so he took a 2x4 and laid it across the edge of the dumpster, and gave it a big karate chop. Since this one was not cut, Tinker almost broke his hand, and yelled and cried for a while. He thought he could chop anything in half with his hand. He could not but he had entertained us anyway.

After while I got a job on the same base with an old high school acquaintance Raleigh. He was famous in high school for having an affair with a young little, blond teacher. Our job was to go around to the Bunkers and load all the dunnage (used lumber) into our dump truck, and dump it at the base dump. It was easy work, and we didn't have much supervision. That base was filthy with deer, and on more than one occasion we found

deer that had been hit and laid next to the road. We loaded it up
and took it to our parking lot, gut it in the woods, and put it in
our car trunk. Good bonus for us, but that job only lasted a
couple of months - then it was back to the docks. I fished for
bottom fish as much as possible, and caught some huge ling cod
off the pier. Another bonus. I found a chicken hen up in the
parking lot, and took it over to my brother Jan's, and gave it to
him. Jan lived in the woods on the edge of town then. He had
shot a pheasant and discovered she was sitting on eggs. He put
the eggs under this chicken in its nest. The chicken hatched, and
raised these pheasants, and it was funny watching the chicken try
to fly like its pheasant young. That was a very successful
experiment on my brother's part as all the young matured and
spread out in the local woods.

     Matt, Jan, one of my uncles named Rod, and I went up to
a lake in the Olympics called Lake Lena, on a fishing trip. It was
a great time and we caught a lot of trout. We left our poles out at
night, and in the morning there would be a drowned trout on the
line for breakfast. Jan always the joker, snuck out at night and
put a gutted, and cleaned, trout on my line. Then when I brought
in my line in the morning, he announced "look at Joey, he
catches trout that are already cleaned"! We hiked up to Upper
Lena, a five mile, straight - up hike, to fish. We could see big
trout but they wouldn't bite on anything we threw at them.
There was an eerie sight up there, as a big old Sichorsky
Helicopter had flown a rescue mission there, and they put it in
the lake. The water was alcohol clear and we could see the
"chopper" in the lake easily. Family trips like this were always
"Golden" to me because I still loved to spend time with my

Brothers'. Uncle Rod's presence was a bonus.

CHAPTER 12

A BOY, A SON, A BOY!

As soon as I got back, I had to rush Litia to the hospital. She was huge, and ready to give birth. My son was born, and they had to use instruments to get him out. His head was all black and blue, misshapen, and he looked like hell. I was so thrilled to have a son, and Litia came through it all just fine. Home we went to resume our life, three of us now! I had been assigned a new job at the Base. I was to work with an old friend. He was a young, lanky guy named Jim; who would end up being one of my life - long friends. Our job was to work at the Base scrap yard. We really never knew what our job was supposed to be, but we made the best of it. To get rid of the boredom we made these big cars with our forklift. We used old car or truck bodies, and put huge locomotive engines, and huge rear ends in them to make these monster - looking autos. I usually brought a couple of "joints" to work with me, but one morning it proved to be my undoing. The FBI was surprise searching at the main gate. They searched me and found my joints in my pocket! I was promptly escorted off the base, and of course lost my job. Jim and I had a lot of fun there, but now that I was a Daddy, I had to get another job pronto.

My next job was picking brush. Salal, and huckleberry are used in floral arrangements. It doesn't pay real well, but I like being in the woods all day, even if I had to wear "rain gear" all day sometimes. There were always deer, bear, eagles, coyote, beaver, mountain beaver, grouse, pheasant, and many other critters out there. It only paid 75cents a hand, and I could usually pick about fifty hands a day. So I wasn't going to get rich, off about 40 dollars a day.

Some of my friends were going down to the Labor Hall in the morning, and getting hired; so I decided to try it again. At that time we were in a depression, and work was hard to find. I got a job squeegeeing the water out of the new Penney's building through the labor hall. That only lasted a couple of weeks, but it was a good amount of pay, I sorely needed. Butch and I started going to the Labor Hall every morning to get work. We went for two weeks and were getting pretty desperate for work. One morning Casey, the head guy there, came in and said "He had work for two guys". We thought we would be sent out to a job, but instead Casey chose two black guys that just came there that morning. We asked Casey "What gives", as he knew we had waited two weeks, and he exclaimed he had to send out "Minorities" to the job. We didn't like being "discriminated against", and decided to look elsewhere.

CHAPTER 13

NORTH TO ALASKA

I heard a bunch of my buddies were getting hired to fight fires in Alaska. The place to go was Fairbanks. I left a little money with Litia; used the rest to fly up to Fairbanks with Duane and Ray. I had a lot of history by then with Duane, and Ray, because Ray was the guy that lived with me for a time, and shot pheasants in our front yard. I sat next to Duane, and Ray sat next to a pretty girl on the plane ride. Ray had our money for some odd reason, and when we arrived we found out he had spent most of our little bit of money, for drinks for that chick. We decided to lose that dope. I never knew what Duane was going to do, especially when he was drinking. When we first got into town, we were walking down the street with just the clothes we were wearing. We came to a cross street called Gobble Street. Since Duane's last name was Gobble, he decided to take all his clothes off, and put them under his arm. There was a hardware store up ahead with a few old black guys sitting in lawn chairs. When Duane and I came by - Duane being fully naked, these guys started laughing and hooting. They were saying things like "Look at this crazy mo fo". It was a wild first experience in Fairbanks. Fairbanks was a "Wide Open" town, and Duane was right at home there. We managed to stay in a real cheap stall in the dark basement of a building on the "main drag". We were to wait for a siren to go off, then go right over to the employment office in the middle of town, and line up. It was only a few hours before the siren went off. We got in line and were issued gear, and went right off to a fire called "The Eagle Creek Fire".

It seemed like half of my buds from Bennington were also on the fire.

They put us in buses and we headed North, past Toke Junction, past North Pole, and out to near the Arctic Circle. Our shift was supposed to be twelve hours on, and twelve hours off, but we worked twenty four hours and more. We were fed a hot meal every third day, but the rest of the time we ate k-rations from the nineteen forties. There's not much food worse than scrambled eggs in a can from 1944. Sometimes we caught rabbits with burned feet, and cooked them up, for a change of menu. The pound cake, and canned meat weren't too bad. On future fires I put ten pounds of spuds, and five pounds of onions in my pack when I left. I also put twenty feet of monofilament line, and some fishing flies in my pack. I tied the fly at the end of the line, with a P-38 can opener about a foot in front of the fly, and tied it to a long stick, and fished for Greyling Trout. There were lots of them in the rivers and creeks, and if I snuck up on them I could catch them. They weren't the best trout, but it was a welcome addition to our diet. I was probably fishing where few had before me.

The boss asked who was familiar with chain saws, and since I was from the Northwest and was familiar with saws and logging, and was appointed chain saw boss. I had Duane, Ray, and Jake the Nut as my crew. The position also came with a raise to sixty four dollars a day - doesn't sound like much, except it was tax free, and accumulated until we were done with the fire - about three weeks on this one. My biggest problem, was keeping the Black Foot Indian Crew from stealing my gas. They stole the gas, threw it in the fire when the wind came up, to keep

the fire going, so they could make more money off the fire.
They kept the Black Foot Indians on one crew by themselves for
good reason. They snuck liquor out on the fire, and would get in
fights, and even stab each other. I guess the bosses decided it
was best for all, to keep them segregated. They shipped the
whole crew up from Montana to fight the fires. Most of our job
consisted of cutting twenty foot wide fire breaks. The trees were
very weenie, as we were so far north, so the job was pretty easy,
and not so heavy. The real problem was the Tundra; it was a
foot or so thick, and had to be cut out a couple of feet wide in the
fire break, by hand with shovel and polaski. Sometimes a fire
could smolder in the Tundra all winter long, then flare-up during
the summer, when the wind came up. When we weren't cutting
fire breaks we walked around with piss-bags, and put out hot
spots. A polaski is an ax with a spade blade on the other side; a
piss-bag was a water reservoir we wore on our back with a small
hose attached. Both tools were well suited for the job.   One of
the worst parts of fighting a fire, was when we had to take a
branch, and beat out a brush fire. The heat was so intense it just
scorched us, even our hair. We had a bad one on the Eagle
Creek Fire that lasted nearly all day. I was so beat at the end of
that day, I just collapsed. The grass fires were just so intense we
tried to avoid fighting them.

        A real young guy walked right into my chainsaw while I
was cutting, and gashed his leg bad, and had to be taken out. We
felt bad for the kid, because they found out he was actually under
eighteen, and was all done fighting fires.

        One of the guys on the crew, was a very old guy. He
was a German soldier during WWII. Another guy was an old
Polish soldier during the war. It was real interesting to hear the

war stories from these two former enemies. The former Polish soldier said "When the Germans first attacked Poland, the Polish soldiers were on horseback, and were being attacked by tanks; which they had never seen before". He said "They were being slaughtered, and found the only way they could take out a tank, was to put a wad of greased rags on a pole, and charge the tank in force". "One of them would get through, and shove the wad of rags up the cannon barrel of the tank causing it to explode when they fired". They had a lot of loss of life, because the Germans were so mechanized and futuristic at warfare.

I asked the former German soldier why the German people would follow a nut like Hitler, and he said "by the time they figured out what a devil he was, he was so powerful, no one could speak-up against him, or they would just disappear". He also said "Hitler even had kids ratting-out their parents". It was all so interesting for me how a bad guy like Hitler could come to power!

We finally finished our "mop-up" on the Eagle Creek fire and headed back to Fairbanks. We all had a nice big check waiting for us.

I didn't hear of any new fires to go out on right away, so I got a plane ticket and headed for Seattle. When I got home I found that Litia, and my son were doing well but really needed money. I had showed up just in time with a good wad of money. I knew my mom would help them while I was gone. She had other Grandchildren, but really "loved" my son as she loved them all. I figured I had about two weeks before I would go back to get on another fire. After I paid all my debts, I still had a good amount of cash left, so I bought a GMC Panel Truck from a guy. It was pretty good running, and had a good looking green body.

The next day I saw my buddy Jim, and he told me "A blues guy named Mississippi Fred O'dowell was playing in a place called Court C in Tacoma". Beings we both were blues fans, we decided to go. Swab and Homo also decided to go. We got some wine; Homo had some good pot and hash. After we got "loaded", we "loaded-up" and headed out in my panel truck. We were playing Led Zeppelins first tape about as loud as it would go, when we decided to pull into a convenience store to get some more wine. I bought the "Ripple" and got back in my panel. I tried to start it but it didn't seem to want to start. After a couple of minutes the clerk from the store came up to my window, and knocked on it. When I rolled it down, she said "It's already running"! We had Led Zeppelin so loud, no one could hear the starter grinding in my window panel.

After a good laugh, we went on to Tacoma. Court C was a tavern in an alley. It had big doors that opened the place up completely to the alley. It was packed so we couldn't get in, but we didn't need to because we had our own wine, and we were still close to the action. When Mississippi Fred came on we rolled a dumpster in front of one of the big open doors; sat on it, and watched a good show for free. He wore one shoe that had a loose sole, so it made a particular sound when he tapped it. He played and sang some of the cool old songs I had on albums at home. We stayed until his last song, then headed out.

On the way back home we took a wrong turn and ended up at the McNeil Island Ferry. McNeil Island was a Federal Prison, and when we pulled down there, a guard with his hand on his gun came out to greet us. We got the hell out of there and got back home in good shape.

The next day there was an outdoor concert in Bennington; headlining a local band that achieved notoriety called the Sonics. Though they had been around awhile I really liked them. Their songs "Psycho" and "The Witch" tore me up. But before they played, there were a couple of opening bands. Between these bands, Duane, Denny, Ray, and a couple of other guys asked "if they could sit in?" The band with the equipment set up gave them the okay. They called themselves "The Funky Fucks" and none of them knew how to play any instrument. They beat, strummed, and banged on all the instruments for a few minutes, making this out-of-whack psychedelic sounds, until it dawned on everyone that they weren't musicians at all; then they pulled the plug on them. That was the first gig for the "Funky Fucks".

A couple of us were salmon fisherman, but didn't put a lot of time into it. We found a charter boat in Westport, skippered by a guy named Frank. Bill, Bill, Les, two other guys I barely knew, and I went down to Westport to Salmon fish for a day. We had three cases of "Rainier Beer" with us, and half - drunk we carried it on the sixty foot boat with us. We were surprised Frank put up with us, but he was extremely patient. First thing leaving the harbor to cross the bar, I started biting the heads off the herring we were to use for bait. This made the bait-boy and the other two guests; a middle aged husband and wife sick. So now the bait-boy was barfing over the side. The couple were passed out in the cabin, and I was putting the bait on everyone's hook. On the way across the bar, I was still biting heads off of herring, and people on other boats could see me. We could hear the captain's radio squawking. "Would you get that guy to stop biting the heads off those herring it's making my guests sick"! I guess the other captains didn't like it. Bill rented a pole on the boat, and after a while he was so drunk he was staggering from one rail to the other across the boat - pole in hand. I heard him say "screw it", and he threw the pole overboard. A short time after that the skipper asked "hey Bill, where's your pole"? It got pretty rough for a while so we all went downstairs, and sat on the benches around the table. The married couple were already there passed out. She had a camera around her neck. Bill took the camera and took pictures of all of us flipping them off. Then he put the camera back around her neck. Imagine their surprise when they had the pictures developed. Anyway we got all our limits of fish and headed in. We were pretty drunk, as we didn't take any beer back. Frank had come through and put up with us again down the road. On future trips when he saw us coming, we could read his lips saying "not these guys again".

My wife, son and I were living in a house a couple of blocks from a big lake. It was just a small, old rental house. It had a big cedar tree in the yard, and the limbs went right to the ground, creating a big hollow underneath the size of a living room. I had a big carpet, furniture, and stereo there, and it was a great party place. One night when it rained too hard to party outside, we were partying inside when my Mom pulled up with my little brother. At that same time Duane took his clothes off, put them under his arm, and stepped out the door. As I was

standing next to her car my Mom shrieks and says "who was
that"? I said "relax it's just Duane".

Duane and I were both broke and decided to go back to
Alaska to get on another fire. It went about as easy as last time,
except we didn't have Ray with us blowing our money. We
ended up sleeping on the Employment Office lawn, because we
didn't have the money for "Bill's Dormitory". We wouldn't
have had any food, except Safeway across the street left their
watermelons out in front in a bin all night. Since the sun never
went down completely it was hot twenty four seven on the lawn.
Duane and I bummed some money, and went to a dance on the
second floor of a building on the main drag. We grabbed a
couple of chicks and were dancing around, when I looked over to
Duane, he's got his pants down, crapping on the floor. I told him
to pull his pants up, and said "let's get out of here". After the
two girls told me the name of the hotel they were living in, we
headed for the stairs out of there. We walked right by two cops
coming up the stairs, because they didn't yet know who they
were looking for.

We did some more drinking then set out to find the two
girls' hotel. They lived on the third floor, so we boarded the
elevator. When we got to the third floor; the door opened and
there were two tough looking red necks coming in. I turned as I
walked past them, and saw Duane crouched in the rear of the
elevator with his back to me doing something. Before I could do
anything about it, the red necks walked past me, and the door
closed. I was pushing the button trying to get the door open,
fearing the worst for Duane. There was scuffling and thuds
coming from the elevator. Finally the door opened and Duane
had one redneck under each arm in a headlock; their faces all

bloody. He said "Joe, what should I do"? I said "drop them and let's get out of here"! We took off down the hall, and the girls we went to visit, stuck their heads out of their apartment door. We asked "how can we get out of here"? They said "there were stairs nearby". We went down the stairs, and as we were going up the side street, we could see the cops entering the front. Duane had huge, wide, hands, and usually either knocked someone out or did serious damage when he punched them. From there we went out to an unfinished ice skating rink outside of town to party some more. Duane and I lost track of each other, and the cops finally caught up to him there. He went to jail, and a couple of days later he went to court. Most all the firefighters from Bennington were there. When the judge asked Duane "why he would do such things" Duane stated "it was the demon rum". He got two weeks in jail, and was there when I went on the next fire.

Jake, Ray, and I were among the crew that were flown by an old Sikorsky Helicopter to a fire above the Arctic Circle out in the middle of nowhere. I was head of the chainsaw crew again, and I had brought a ten pound bag of spuds, and five pounds of onions in my pack. Combined with the canned meat from the sea rations it made a pretty good stew. Something to off-set our trout and rabbit dinners.

Denny also wasn't with us because he also got arrested and thrown in jail in an unrelated incident.

We had to cut a lot of fire breaks in a hurry to stay ahead of the fire. They started telling us to "cut the tundra' with our chainsaws. That was a dumb idea, as the saws got so dull so quick, we were spending all our time sharpening our saws.

We had a guy from Iran with us named "Emmy". He was a pretty talented guy, and was great at sticking knives in targets. He could stick a knife in a target at fifty feet throwing bent over between his legs. It has always made me question what we are being told about Iranians as Emmy was such a good guy.

One guy was particularly annoying, because he decided he was going to be a boss, and was always trying to boss everyone around. Nut decided to do something about him, and crapped in his mummy bag. We all crawled in our sack early and waited for this guy to crawl in his bag. In a while he came along, and slipped into his bag. When he complained about someone crapping in his bag, we all "busted up" laughing. He kinda faded away after that.

About a couple of weeks into the operation, Emmy, Nut and me got over run by the fire. I could hear trees exploding above us faster than we could run. We dropped our saws and took off on a diagonal course. We finally started to get out of its' path, as the wind eased some, and it had passed us by. After we put the fire out, we could only find the blade, chain, and some motor parts left in the ashes.

Unfortunately it had burned our camp completely out. I think the "Blackfeet" had thrown some gas on the fire when the wind came up, but I couldn't be sure. It had almost cost some of us our life, and we weren't too happy. We had no sleeping bags, food, or any personal stuff left - not even clothes except what was on our back. We kept a big fire going and slept around the edge of it to keep warm. It was July and it was still dry, but it got down to near freezing at night. They dropped sea rations and sleeping bags from a cargo plane eventually, but the first forty eight hours or so, were pretty miserable.

We finally "mopped up" the fire and hiked to a nearby village where we loaded onto an old DC-3 aircraft. They flew us to Fairbanks, and safety! They gave us some extra money for our personal stuff we lost, so I had a nice fat check the next day. We learned Duane was still in jail, and since he had gotten two weeks jail time, and we were gone three weeks, we wondered why? Seems when Duane got out of jail for his original two weeks, he got drunk, and went back to the same dance hall, and crapped on the floor again; so the judge threw him in jail for another three weeks. I guess the judge viewed him as a slow learner.

We waited around for a new fire to go out on, but the fires were winding down and we still weren't on one by the time Duane and Denny were out of Jail.

When the cops put Denny in jail they hadn't noticed a big bowie knife on Denny's side. They saw it when he was in the cell, and told him to hand it to them. He told them to "come in and get it - I just want to stick you with it"! That didn't go over well, but now he was out.

We were listening to a lot of "Creedence Clearwater Revival" at this time, as "Willy and the Poorboys" was just out. Duane really liked "Dr John the Night Tripper". He was always playing "Walk on Guilded Splinters". We had started listening to Creedence on my first trip to Alaska. We were between fires, and we heard that if a cabin had no door, we could stay in it. So of course Duane tore the door off a cabin in the woods north of town. About twenty of us moved in and around the cabin.

Homo, always having the latest music, had a tape of Willy and the Poor Boys and Bayou Country, and we played the hell out of it. We had a good bon fire going when we heard something big come through the bushes. A big cow moose and its' young one, came running right through our campfire. We were all diving for cover as the cow moose was the size of a horse and the calf wasn't much smaller. After the scene calmed down a cruiser with a couple of Alaska Troopers showed up. We were informed we couldn't stay even if the door was off the cabin. We said "we would leave", but we didn't until the next day.

That wasn't the only situation we had with a moose. Denny and Paul had driven a little Morris Minor up the Alcan Highway to get to Fairbanks. Duane, Denny, Homo, and I were riding north of town one day when a huge bull moose ran out, and attacked the car. We rolled up the windows and he put his head and massive horns right through the radiator. Then he started attacking the side. We thought that was the time to escape out the other side. Denny's Morris was destroyed so we just left it there on the road. Last we saw the moose was still "taking" his car out.

A former boss told us he could get us on a fire in a couple of days. The fires were kinda fought that way - the payola, good old boy system. Seemed corrupt to me, but we all needed a fire. He had an old Quonset hut outside of town, we could stay in until we went on the fire. He transported Duane, Denny, Nut, Ray, another few guys, and I out to the Quonset hut. We only had limited food, mainly sea rations, so we started scheming on other food. We could hear chickens nearby, so Duane and I headed that way. There was a farm with lots of chickens, so we grabbed a couple and headed back. We plucked them outside, then cut them up, and threw them in a frying pan. They were tough but good. An Alaskan State Trooper pulled in, with another guy in the passenger side of his car. The trooper tried to get us to "fess up" about the chickens, but to no avail. The guy in the car on the passenger side, was evidently the owner of the farm we swiped the chickens from. When the trooper told him he couldn't do anything about the chickens, as he didn't have enough evidence; the guy started "freaking out". I think he had an epileptic fit, because he started kicking the crap out of the inside of the cruiser, and the trooper stepped out and just closed the door, and let him go at it. The trooper called for backup on his hand held radio, and soon another cruiser arrived. After a while everyone calmed down and they all left. We all laughed, because we thought chicken crackling in the frying pan, and feathers all over out front, was enough evidence. The guy never got us on a fire, so after a couple of days we went back to town.

We heard if we could get to Anchorage, they were still fighting fires on the Kenai. We didn't have any money, because I had sent most of my check home. We decided to get on the train that went from Fairbanks to Anchorage. There were about eight of us that decided to sneak on the train. We just kept changing seats and it worked for everyone except Dement. He got caught and the last time I saw him he was thrown off in a little village called "Happy", that was served by only the train and "bush pilots". It was very remote and only had about eighty residents, and I'll never forget seeing Dement surrounded by locals as we were pulling away. Funny thing was I ran into Dement on Northern Lights Boulevard in Anchorage a month later, and he was already a part owner in a pool hall. Dement was a guy from back home, and the only thing I knew about him was he had pulled his van over to the side of the road back home, because he had a flat tire. When he returned someone had rolled the van over, and it had ended up "tits up" in a swamp. During that time he had been out visiting Jon, Alan, Dirty Ned, Paul and Skip out at a creek named Gold Creek. They were camped there and the powers - that - be didn't like it. The local paper had declared if they wanted to get the hippies out of Gold Creek "all they had to do was throw a bar of soap in the creek". Very Funny!

When Duane, Denny, and I first got to Anchorage we found a Salvation Army with a hot food cafeteria, and we managed to eat a hot meal. We met a guy there that called himself "Celery Stalk" for want of a better name. When I asked his name he seemed to say the first thing that came to mind. He was an easy going, fun loving hippie. He told us he was staying at a "crash pad", and he thought there was room for us. Duane and Denny wanted to go down the street for something. I elected to stay there and agreed to meet them there later. About an hour later I looked down the street from the way they went, and it looked like two "Riverboat Gamblers" walking toward me. Duane and Denny had walked into a second hand store, and put on these black, pinstripe, duds with vests and black cowboy hats. I was impressed.

We went over to the "crash pad" and found "Celery Stalk". We were able to stay there, and it was a nice two story house that was owned by a guy named Hester. Hester was a forty year old black guy, who was a Unitarian Life Minister. He had a bedroom locked up, upstairs and said "we were

welcome but to stay away from upstairs". After a few days he
told Duane and I, he had to go to the "lower forty eight" for a
public speech. Evidently he made his living doing just that. He
said "he would pay all the bills, and he liked us, and would
leave the house in our control". What a sweet deal that was for
us. Besides "Celery Stalk", there was a girl that reminded me
of Janis Joplin, and a couple of other guys. We bid goodbye to
Hester, and told him not to worry. We noticed he had
padlocked his bedroom door upstairs.

      Our next hurdle consisted of finding a job, as there was
snow on the ground - so no fires. I heard we might find a job at
a cold storage place across from the airport. We got the jobs,
and were to work in a forty degrees below zero freezer, taking
food in and out. It was mostly seafood, but also had Continental
Cuisine meals stored there for the airlines. It was perfect,
because we could stash crab, lobster, fish, scallops, or
Continental Cuisine meals out back to take to our "crash pad"
after work. Sometimes I worked on the fish gutting line right
next to the oriental workers. When that happened we got fresh
salmon to take home.

      Back at Hester's crash house, we started hanging with a
big Indian we called "Cold Turkey". Denny had already headed
south to Bennington. "Cold Turkey" was a drunk that would go
into drinking places on 4th Avenue, and grab other small Indians
and turn them upside down and shake the money out of them. If
we hung with him we could always get money to drink. He
always said "Wild Turkey at night, and Cold Turkey in the
morning". He drank "Wild Turkey Whiskey" exclusively.
Duane got caught putting a case of lobster out the back door, so
he got fired, and I quit. It was below zero out, and we decided it

was time to head back south. I needed to spend time with my wife and son. We said "bye" to everyone at the "crash pad" and went to the airport. I never noticed the huge stuffed polar bear in the Anchorage Airport before. It must be ten feet tall and near a ton in weight. It is standing in an "attack" position; very impressive.

When I got back I didn't do anything for a couple of days. I heard a local muffler shop needed an installer, so I went down to apply.

CHAPTER 14

"HERSHEY"

When I went in I was met by an old guy name Hershey. Right off I could tell he was a character, and he proved to be just that. He hired me, because he knew I had gas and arc welding experience because of my job at the yard. I even told him "I was fired", and he didn't hold it against me. He lived in Seattle, and rode the ferry to the shop each day in time to open at 9 a.m. It was kind of a dirty job, but it was a pretty good job. It paid well, and Hershey was a good guy to work for. He was also an auctioneer, and was able to do his auctioneering with a cigarette hanging out of his mouth. I liked to watch him when salesmen came in, and he gave them a hard time, and they wouldn't even realize it because he was so smart. After a couple of months, he let me open, and handed over more duties to me. I got good at exhaust systems for Harleys, and did them after hours sometimes.

We had a fifteen gallon bottle to make wine in at home. Somehow it plugged and blew up while we were gone. We came home to a foul smelling front room with wine everywhere, and foam in the corners. We decided to move and found a small house near Silverville on the Bay.

Litia, my son, and I went to an indoor fair at the fairgrounds. There was a guy there with a booth, selling lots on Lake Symington about twenty minutes from town. I could get a lot for $ 25.00 a month; so I couldn't see how I could go wrong;

so I bought it. It turned out to be a good move because I partied there on the lot, and eventually built a house there.

That next day there was a story in the paper that read "Local man tries to commit suicide by jumping off ferry". It was Duane, but I knew something wasn't right, as Duane wasn't the type to try suicide. When I read on, the article stated that they had lowered the rescue boat, and that he was arrested when they got to Bennington. I believed the part about him getting arrested, but the real story was that he, Denny, and Nut were drunk and throwing bottles of Rainier Beer to each other on the top deck. One got by Duane and he fell over trying to get it.
That story sounded more like Duane!

I got a crock and another fifteen gallon bottle and started making wine again. I had good parties, and sometimes my wine wouldn't even get done, before Dirty Ned, Alan, Red, Skip, and others would come over to party, and start siphoning the unfinished wine out of the fifteen gallon bottle. The stuff got us drunk, but we got the "shits". AKA "Green Mountain Skidders". Sometimes we bought PCP joints for a buck each from a guy I met named "Randy Rat". He lived about ten minutes away in a house with Robby, Kent and his girl Alice. That stuff really got me "high". It was a liquid that was dropped on mint leaves, and rolled. We got so high at my house once, I was palms up on the low ceiling, and didn't know why. Everyone else was doing the same thing! Like we were holding the ceiling up. I was coming back from getting some PCP when I saw a raccoon laying in the middle of the road. I picked it up and tossed it in the back seat. A mile or so later it came to, and started growling and hissing. I got it home, put it in a cage, and tried to make a pet of it. That never worked, and I finally had to let it go. My friend Red did have a pet one. I went over to his house, or I should say "his Dad's house", and this small raccoon ran loose inside. He played rough, and there was always lots of shredded paper all over the floor. It was hell on my arms, because he scratched me when I played with him, but it was fun. Dirty Ned, Allan, John, Red, Bill, came over one eve, when I had a bunch of wine that was done. We got some PCP from Robby. We drank and smoked all night, and about six in the morning, we ran out of wine, and jumped in Red's van and left to get more. There was a plastic Viking helmet, and a kind of cloth thing made to hang on a wall that read "Better Dead than Red" in the van. I put the helmet complete with horns on. We were on the freeway, and hadn't made it to the store yet, when the wheel fell off. I was holding up the cloth wearing the helmet and making an ass of myself, when an infamous state patrolman pulled up. After a couple of other cruisers pulled up, a rumble ensued and we were all taken to jail. We continued the rumble at the jail, and even in the jail, when we found out there was a "rat" inside. We kinda worked him over pretty good.   We got out the next day, but were each given some jail time by the judge. Allan got more because he was really out-of-control through it all, and refused to move on his own and the cops carried him kicking into the cell.

A couple of weeks later I went to a dance at the local dance hall. I got drunk and high, and managed to get in a fight inside. A Sheriff's Deputy I knew, named Jack, came along and threw both of us combatants in his car. Halfway to jail I told Jack I had to "wiz" and he had to stop. He refused and said "I just had to hold it". Well I couldn't and pulled it out and wizzed on the floor. When we got to the jail, Jack told me I had to clean it up. I took off running, and he shot in the air. The loud "boom" startled me so bad I fell down. He tackled me, cracked me on the head with his gun, and threw me in the tank. When I went to court the cop read all this stuff I did for the court. The judge was Myron Froyd, who was actually pretty easy on me. I was surprised! At an earlier time when that judge was a prosecutor, he was portrayed in the paper, as having pulled a pair of scissors on someone. I called him up and asked "if he wanted to buy a pair of switchblade scissors". He didn't think it was very funny. There was to be another "Rock Festival" in nearby Eatonville, called the Buffalo Party Convention, on July 3rd, 4th, and 5th. The cops tried to stop this one at first; but gave up after a while, as everyone just drove around the road block or just parked and walked in. I had bought a 500 Triumph motor cycle, and drove it in on a dirt back road.

This place was stunningly beautiful because it was on a ranch, with about eighty buffalo, three ponds, and Mount Rainier at the end of the valley. There was also a river nearby. There was an entry fee that was easy to get around. Scheduled to play was Quick Silver Messenger Service, Moby Grape, a lot of Seattle bands, including One Hand Clapping. James Cotton Blues Band played on the 4th of July at midnight. They were trying to start a new political party. The bands were great and there was a guy that sang and played the blues, on his guitar that was especially "cool". On the fourth of July at midnight, fireworks' started going off, and James Cotton Blues Band took the stage. Talk about cool!

That was my first experience with the "bean lady". She sold a bowl of beans for twenty five cents, and that was the only nourishment I had there.

The cops were flying overhead, and dropping leaflets that stated "it was an illegal gathering, and we had to leave". We just dropped our drawers and showed them our ass! After a couple of days, the fish in the ponds died, and were floating on top. After all these "hippies" bathing in the ponds, and a couple of motorcycles went in, it was just too much for the fish. In order to walk in to the festival, I had to walk across a wooden bridge that had a bulldozer turned sideways to keep the cops from coming in. This river had a waterfall on it, and a guy slipped in the moss at the top, and fell to his death. Fortunately that was the only tragedy.

There was a lot of liquor and drugs that were mostly free, and that wasn't lost on Treptoes who was either "jammin hard" or passed out on the ground for three days. I did a fair job of "jammin" myself.

This was a beautiful festival. I have always been so glad I was able to attend. Three days of love, music, drugs and good times - what could be better for a young guy?

It was time to leave so I tied my bag to the sissy bar and prepared to leave. A girl I met wanted a ride to Tacoma; and since it was on the way I agreed. I continued home, and decided it was time for me to pay more attention to Litia and my son. I settled down some; worked and started Cutthroat Trout fishing in front of my house. I got pretty good at it, and really enjoyed eating the fresh trout.

My son was getting to be a few months old, and was developing a personality. I really loved that boy.

This was a great time for music. The Beatles, Stones,

Creedence Clearwater, The Who, Canned Heat, Doors, Quick Silver Messenger Service, and Clapton among others were all making great music during these times.

I was able to get tickets to see Ten Years After in Seattle; so I decided Litia needed some fun, and we went. Fortunately my Mom loved to watch my son anytime. When we got to the Seattle Center, there was a riot going on over something. Maybe because it was "sold out", and Rock-n-Rollers just wanted to get in. At any rate when we were walking to the Coliseum, I had to hold the tickets up to keep from getting our heads busted by the cops. Ten Years After was great, and I had never seen anyone play guitar as fast as Alvin Lee on "Going Home". His hands were just a blur.

We did a little partying when we got back to town, because we didn't have to pick up my son until the next day. The next concert we attended, was to see Canned Heat in Seattle. This time I was with Bill, Marvin, Jim; a whole bunch of us that appreciated the blues. "On the Road Again" was good of course, but we really liked hearing some of the less played songs like "Anphetamine Annie", "Bull Frog Blues", and so on. Wilson of the Canned Heat was one of the four that all died in the same year at 27 years old. Janis Joplin, Jimi Hendrix, and Jim Morrison being the other three.

I had seen Janis Joplin a couple of years earlier at an upstairs venue called the Firestone Theatre with The Iron Butterfly opening. The Iron Butterfly had a long trough on the front of the stage with some sort of fuel in it that was on fire. I could hardly believe it was allowed, since the theatre was up a long zig-zag hallway that went up a ways, with no other way out.

If that place would have started on fire, we would have burned like rats. When Big Brother and the Holding Company came on, Janis of course had her usual pint of Southern Comfort whiskey, and was drinking and talking her kind of "squeaky" talk. They were all great, but I think the long version of "Inna-Godda-DaVita" stole the show.

I was getting real good at patching exhaust systems at work, and a lot of used car lots would have me patch up their vehicles exhaust. One of them was Leon Wolf, one of three brothers I knew. Leon was a real good stock car driver, and usually won any race he was in. Jim Wolf owned a tavern, and Bobby Wolf ran with a guy called "Joker". The three of us hung out together some. Bobby and Joker were real good drivers, and drove through people's yards, off of jumps onto the next lawn. They had kind of like courses through the neighborhood. They knew a girl they called "Sunday Punch". She lived with her mom and when her mom went to church, they went over and got it on with her. I went over with them to "Sunday Punch's" house one Sunday. They both took their turns, and while Bobby was with her, Joker and I got some eggs and hamburger out of the fridge and started tossing them at each other. By the time Bobby was done, we had eggs and hamburger stuck all over the walls. So when "Sunday Punch's" mom got home after we'd gone, her daughter was all "slimed" out and the house was trashed with food.

I was taking my little brother up to a low-income neighborhood, and letting him drive my car around. He was only about fifteen years old. He did well right from the start, and he really thought he was "cool".

I had an injury at work that got me a couple of days off. I drove a Thunderbird onto the rack, and left it running so I could find the leaks when I ran it up. When I got out of the car, and had put it in park, it "popped" into reverse on its own, and backed up which crushed me between the car door and one of the main stanchions on the left. It knocked me out cold, and wiped out the car door. It was painful to breathe for a couple days, so Hershey gave me a couple of days off.

CHAPTER 15

SKY RIVER III

There was starting to be talk of another rock festival to be called Sky River III. The state threw a fit about the previous ones, so the organizers decided to be a little sneakier about it. They had a guy, fictitiously named "Dancing Bear" that came on one of Seattle's rock stations at noon each day before the event. He would tell facts about the upcoming festival, but not give the date or where it was to be at. He claimed The Youngbloods, Jefferson Airplane, Big Brother and the Holding Company, B.B. King as well as some others were to perform there. Finally when the event got closer he said it was to be about one week long and would include Labor Day Weekend. Finally the day before it was to start, he said "it will be near Washougal, Washington on a farm". It was a good tactic, because it didn't give counties much of a chance to get the legal wheels rolling against it. As a result there weren't any road blocks that I saw, because as usual the cops were overwhelmed by hoards' of people.

Jon, Allan, Dirty Ned, Skip and I set out for the festival in my panel truck down I-5. We got down to Kalama when a few of us needed to relieve ourselves. I pulled over on a vacant side road, and we lined up and started "wizzing" off the road. A deer had been laying there, and we spooked him. He took off running and I reached down, and grabbed a big rock, and let it fly. What a shot - I nailed it right in the head on the run - and down it went. Before it could get up, Ray grabbed my tire iron and did it in. Jon had a buck knife with him, so we dragged the deer to the brush, and cut all four quarters, the neck, and back strap off it. We had a good amount of meat before we even got to the festival.

Skip managed to get a huge American Flag, that used to fly over the Naval Yard, and we set about putting up a big tent, on the side of the slope, overlooking the stage. Our tent was right in the center and visible from almost anywhere.

The weather wasn't co-operating for this one, because it was cooler and wetter than normal. At least on Labor Day weekend it wasn't too bad. To my relief the Bean Lady was also at this one. We cooked that deer over open fires, and it went pretty quick.

They were telling everyone from the stage over the p.a. to be careful, that there were some bad "Merican Reds" circulating. There were overdoses going on, and many people were walking O.D'd people around to keep them alive. I met up with an old friend - Jerry, and we decided to pool our money and buy all the wine we could, and open a wine booth. We jumped into Jerry's VW, and went to the nearest liquor store. We found they were already out of every wine, except for the gallons. Jerry and I bought about 100 gallons, and thought we would sell it for a dollar a fifth - bring your own bottle. It worked like a champ, and we had people bring their own bottle, and we filled them up. Our goal was not to make any money, but to have free wine. There was a constant party going on inside our booth. My buddy Butch, was barking about our wine most of the time to the crowd. "Get your wine here - one dollar a fifth". This one guy and his chick, kept coming back for more, until I heard him put his bottle down on the counter to be refilled, but when I stood up to refill his bottle, he wasn't there. I looked over the counter, and they were both crumpled up on the ground below - passed out! It was a good way to party with a lot of people and we kept it up until the vino was gone.

Turned out Jefferson Airplane, and Big Brother and the Holding Company didn't make it. It could have been the crappy weather, or the fact that at the same time Santana was playing a festival called Vortex in Oregon. Maybe they went there to play because the weather was better.

The Youngbloods with Jesse Young showed up, as well as B.B. King, and it was very good. There was a bunch of notasfamous and local bands that also performed. There was nonstop entertainment except when the rain shorted out the electrical on stage.

There were O.D. people, babies born there, and unfortunately one guy got too high, and drowned in the Washougal River. As usual there were some problems with the bikers, assaults, attempted rapes and such.

Crosby, Stills, Nash, and Young were stated to show up, but that didn't happen, at least not that I ever saw but most of that time was just a blur anyway.

One afternoon we were sitting in front of our big flag tent, watching and listening to music. A fairly new convertible pulled in below us and the three occupants sat up on the car and watched the show. The paint job on the car looked a little weird, and I thought one of the guys looked familiar. On further look - it was Denny. I went down to say "hello" and noticed the car looked like it had been painted with poof-cans. The story was Denny had swiped the car in Alaska and spray painted it himself, and put a bogus license plate on it. I wondered why it looked like it was wired on right over the old plate. He had driven through corn fields around border crossings, and driven down here just in time for the festival. As wild as Denny was I was sure it was true.

I heard when the festival was over he drove up to Seattle and sold it to a guy for a thousand dollars and went to Hawaii on the money. The schmuck that bought it from him got busted. It all sounded like something Denny would do.

Near the end of this festival, it got pretty foul, because the local law had an injunction on the festival. No new sani - cans, and no garbage were hauled out. To make things worse the garbage pile started on fire and a big stinky cloud of smoke moved over the place. It stunk for quite a while! All in all it was a lot of fun, and I felt so good I lived in a time when I could go to these festivals. Other generations, before and after, would not be able to attend these gatherings as they no longer exist in America.

Finally I hopped on my Triumph and went back home; winter was on the way and I needed to get myself together, and get a little more serious about my Litia and son. It was good to have a job to go back to that I liked. For now this job was alright. My buddy Jim stopped by work sometimes. He had a little sports car and pulled in with the top down. He was wearing this bill hat that had shades hooked right to the bill. He could just fold them down to use them. I think he thought his hat/sunglasses were pretty unique, and they were! One night I came home to an empty house. I called around and found that Litia had gone to a party with my son. I didn't like that much, and went there myself. Everyone, including Litia was very drunk. To my disappointment my son had been laid out on the bed in the bedroom, near a passed out guy I didn't recognize.

When I saw this I came unglued, and chewed Litia's ass,
grabbed my son and left. Anyone could have stumbled into the
dark bedroom, and fallen on my son; or the drunk stranger could
have molested my son. When she finally showed up at home, I
let her know she was never to take our son to a party again.
She was getting real lazy, and spent most of her time sleeping. I
was getting real tired of it. After a couple of weeks, she took
my son to another party, and laid him on a bed again. This was
the "last straw", and I wasn't going to allow her to put my boy's
life in danger again - so I kicked her out. She went to live with
her mom and started looking for a job.   She didn't seem to care
too much about being separated from her son, and I sensed that
she didn't love her son that much. I still let her have my son, but
only if her mom was present for visits. Her mom assured me
she would not let Litia take my son out. It seemed to take care
of the problem and I didn't feel his life was in danger any
longer.

This old guy I knew from hanging at Litia's aunt's house
had died. Jim was 78 years old, and he and I smoked pot
together sometimes. We took a lid up to Irene's at
Thanksgiving, and everyone got high. Jim smoked with us. His
huge wife would come in down the hall, bitching about Jim
smoking pot, and grab him by the arm, and haul him out. Like I
say, she was huge, probably three hundred fifty or more pounds
dry. When she stomped down the hall, the whole house shook.
We always got a good laugh at the spectacle.

James also hung out up there. He was a country music
singer, who had formerly been a Sherriff's Deputy from a nearby
county. He was fond of pot also and had been fired for being
high. He told me of some of his exploits being high on the job,

and made country songs out of some of the experiences.
My mom watched my son while I went to work, and all was
good for a while. I finally let Bill, Daviduke, and another friend
move in with me to help pay the bills.

Just after I got to work one morning I got a phone call
from Bill stating my house had burned to the floor! Seems
Daviduke had rolled over in his sleeping bag, and his bag caught
on fire from a space heater - then he rolled back and little fires
shot out everywhere. When the fire finally woke them, there
were fires going all over the bedroom, as well as on Daviduke's
bag.

When I got out there later on, only the floor was left
with the refrigerator still standing. To my surprise there was an
unopened bottle of wine that was still cold. I opened it and took
a drink with Bill and Daviduke, but it tasted like smoke. Now
that my son and I didn't have a home I pondered my next move.
The Red Cross helped us with some clothes and food. Allan,
Dirty Ned, Jon, and skip had a place in town, and let Bill, my
son and myself stay for a while. Bill opted to stay mostly with
his girlfriend.

We ended up going back and renting my old place on
Broad Street. Life was pretty good for my son and I there for a
while, and sometimes Daviduke stayed for a day or two when he
wasn't working as a carnie.

Eventually Litia got pissy about not having her son with
her. I think her Mom and friends were getting on her case;
because I don't think she really cared that much. I decided to
leave the area with my son, because I knew right now I had as
much right to my son as she did, but if she filed for custody that
could change I didn't want to get in a "pissing match" with her

and her family. Daviduke wanted to leave also, as his car had died when he got there. So Daviduke and I loaded my Triumph 500 and my son in my window panel delivery. I left my keys on the counter at Hershey's shop. I hadn't told anyone about my plans except for my mom.

CHAPTER 16

ON THE ROAD AGAIN

One of the first things I saw when we reached Idaho, was a "red-neck" looking truck with a "red-neck" driving that had a peace symbol spray painted on the tailgate that read "Footprint of the American Chicken". I didn't get a good feeling about seeing this. We headed for the center of town, and since it was on a big lake I knew there would be a good park, with a good beach.

When we got there we relaxed on the beach. Daviduke took off and I left my son on the sand with some toys. I swam out to a raft about forty feet away, and lay back and watched my son, while I got some rays. After I'd relaxed for maybe a half hour, I see this old fat lady walk up to my son and, take his hand, and start walking away. I dove right in and caught up with the lady. I grabbed her shoulder, spun her around, and asked, "Lady. Where are you going with my son"? She answered "you were not taking care of him"! I told her "if I weren't watching my son, how come I was on you so quick"? I told her I should have her arrested for child kidnapping. She got right out of there, but this sure left a bad taste in my mouth. My entry into Cour D Alene was red-neck trouble so far.

I tracked down Daviduke and we headed east along the lake. When we got to the corner of the lake, about to leave it, there was a little community. A few houses, a couple of small businesses, and a public dock on the lake. One of the buildings was built to look like a long fish. We took a look at it, and decided it was a "closed" restaurant with a lot of the building vacant. I found the owner, a middle aged lady, and asked about renting it. She rented it to me for $100 a month, along with some manual labor from us. We kinda hung sheets to divide the place into two rooms. She was a very nice lady, and didn't ask for too much labor. She wouldn't allow any parties there, so we only stayed about a month.

We noticed a rent sign on a house boat at the pier. It was just one large room, but we could party here and the rent was also $100. We divided it into two rooms with sheets again. We had to walk up to the foot of the dock to use the sani-can. We just kept a bar-b-que on the deck, and used a hot plate for food because it had electricity. We copped a stereo and a couple of couches, chairs, and mattresses. Soon we were moved in! We hung a lot in Cour d Alene and soon met lots of people. We met one particular freak named Bob. He was long haired, kind of a weenie, and liked to party. Pretty soon we were having Bob and a few others we met over for parties. We'd met three or four cute girls, and were honing in on two of them. Georgia and Penny were both very good looking girls, but sort of snobbish. We heard Savoy Brown was going to play Spokane. I wanted to see them, since I always liked their album "Street Corner Talking". We asked the girls if they wanted to go, and we did go a couple of Saturday nights later.

We didn't particularly like the venue. It was just kind of a big, plain, old building. The band sounded great - even the opening band. I noticed the lead singer had a pair of tall, checkerboard, leather boots on. We danced around and sipped off the wine we smuggled in. Just before the concert ended, a girl came up and invited us to a party afterwards. She gave us directions, so when it was completely over, encore and all, we headed out to the party. We got there with no problems. When we knocked on the door a guy welcomed us in. Right away I spotted the checkerboard leather boots, standing in the corner. Evidently at least the Savoy Brown singer, was there. After we got situated we noticed all the band were there; along with a few women, and a couple of roadies.

Daviduke and I kinda lost track of the girls after a while. They were all over the band. I noticed Daviduke was sitting at a phone desk looking at something. Simmons, the guitar player, came over to Daviduke, and grabbed his passport out of Davidukes's hand, and started reading him the "riot act". Daviduke offered up some bogus excuse, how it just "fell into his hands"! He was told to leave, so I left with him, and the women stayed behind. I think that was the plan from the beginning, because I couldn't figure why we were invited to the party, except they wanted our women.

Daviduke had a carnival to work in Spokane that would last about two weeks. He asked if I wanted to work the carnival. I'd never done it before, so I decided to give it a try.

Bob said his mom, whom I had met before, would watch my son for a bit of money. We didn't want to go back and forth so it was decided we would come back one Sunday evening in the middle of the run.

I got put in a "Throw Baseballs in the Basket" booth with my buddy. We had to eat a lot of "Dex" to get through all those hours of talking. We made pretty good money at first but got "burned out" as it got to the end.

The whole object was to never let anyone win, because the prizes cost us money. We stashed money or H.O and only handed over most of it to the boss. Once I "fouled" a girl, so we wouldn't have to give her a prize, and she got so pissed she slung a baseball out of the crowd later. She would have "nailed" me if Daviduke hadn't warned me because he saw her winding up out of the corner of his eye. We finally tore everything down, and headed toward our houseboat on the lake. I really missed my boy and could hardly wait to see him.

We got to Bob's moms house, and when we went to the door she told me he'd gotten sick and had to be put in the hospital. We went right to the hospital, and when I got there, my boy was in a crib that was like a cage. He saw me walk in and started yelling "dad"! They said "he had a severe cold", which was news to me, because he was fine a week earlier when I last saw him. When I tried to take him home, I was told the Welfare Department had a hold on him, and we had to talk to welfare the next morning.

We did that and found out Bob's mom was a whacko, and had told the Welfare Department I abandoned my son. She was trying to collect welfare for him. She was full of crap, because she knew exactly where we were, and even had a phone number for us. They let me take him with me to the houseboat the next day. Seemed like Idaho was full of "red-necks". Even the women seemed like "red-necks".

A couple nights later we went into the park, and Daviduke latched onto a good looking girl. She said "she wanted to stop by our houseboat the next day". Bob stayed with us that night. Next morning the girl showed up about nine in the morning. She brought a lid of grass with her, sat it on the coffee table, then said "she had to go to the parking lot and get some papers out of her car". She never came back and we used none of that lid. Seemed very odd that she left it and never came back!

We decided to wash our laundry, so Bob, Daviduke, my son and I, walked up, got in our car, and before we could pull out, the cops surrounded our car, and stuck their guns in our faces. "Freeze Hippies", and "out of the car and on the ground longhairs"! They said they were taking us in for drug possession.

The cops had me cuffed with my son sitting on my lap. They searched our place and only found some cocaine in Bob's wallet and the lid the girl had brought over.

They released us later. We were on O.R. and had to get a lawyer. The lawyer we got was a young guy wearing long hair, a corduroy suit and a little "stash bag" on his belt. A lawyer trying to look like a hippie?

We finally went to court and obviously they had to cut us loose. We were about as "set up" as you can get. We heard that girl left the lid to set us up, because her brother was a local cop, and she wanted to make him "look good". Also Daviduke and Bob were shooting off their mouths about cocaine. They had gone back to Bennington, and evidently brought back some "coke". I didn't like them going back to Bennington anyway, because I feared one or both would shoot off their mouths about where I was.

I hated to leave the houseboat because it was quiet and a good place to fish, but we had enough of Idaho, and decided to move to Spokane.

CHAPTER 17

SPOKANE FALLS

We headed to one of my aunt's house to see Lottie and her husband Harry. He was kind of a "hair-lip" and pronounced his name "Hawwy". My aunt was a good looking, strong headed woman, who suffered from diabetes. They were both retired, and my aunt had too much time on her hands, and was prone to drinking mixed drinks. She had retired from the phone company. We also went over to see my cousin Terry, whom I was very close to, until she moved out of the area when we were about five years old. My grandpa and grandma watched us during our early years, while our moms worked. My Aunt Lottie's first husband Duey was quite a character, because he had so many diverse jobs before he died. He had been a hair dresser, a bomb shelter builder, and had owned a potato chip company, just a block away from my grandparent's house. My granny took Terry and I over to Duey's potato chip company, and we ate some right off the conveyor belt while they were still warm. You've never had potato chips until you have eaten them this fresh.

My cousin shocked me when she asked if Daviduke and I were gay! I think she thought that because we lived together, we must be gay. Absurd!

We had scored a rental house in a "middle class" neighborhood in a Spokane suburb. It had a heated basement for us to jam and make wine. The woman that owned the house also owned a dump nearby. She gave us all the beds and furniture we needed. It was good except a couch she gave us looked okay but it was loaded with fleas, so we had to get it out of there right away.

My buddy Bill had a good looking cousin named Sharri. He was evidently "fooling" around with her. After he left town to go back to Bennington, we asked her and her good looking blond friend out. We took the two, to a local bar that had a good rock band. Daviduke latched on to Sharri, while I hung with Jill. It became apparent after a while, we should switch. I liked Sharri better anyway, because she really was a "10". One thing led to another, and she became my girlfriend. Daviduke and Jill didn't "pan out" long term.

We both enrolled in school at Spokane Falls College. I had the G.I. bill going for me so I didn't have to pay anything. Pete got some sort of aid, so he didn't pay much. We had three classes, but we enjoyed the political science the most. If Daviduke was good at anything, it was talking, and arguing, and those skills really came in handy in this class.

We managed to score some "acid" and got our girls together, took my son to my cousins, and went out on the town. About halfway through the night at the bar, we "dropped" the "acid". It was "window paine" and was pretty clean. It made the road roll up and down like the ocean. Also everything was distorted. We were glad Sharri was driving her car. It was a big old battleship looking Ford. That was only about the third time I took "acid" and I liked the "high", but didn't want to make a "habit" of it, because I knew it couldn't be good for my body and my mind in the "long haul"..

Another time at the bar, we couldn't even find our car when we came out, and had to come back the next day to find it.

Our place was a good "party house", and we had the basement set up real fine. Just like my old place in Silverville, friends came over when they knew my wine was ready. My son was getting obsessed with trains. When I got up in the morning, he had every small item he could get a hold of, lined up across the floor, like a train. I decided to take my son on a train trip to my friend Tom's house, across the bay from Bennington.

Because my son liked to jump like a frog, I nicknamed him "Frog". Sharri, Frog, and I got on the train in Spokane. I don't think Frog realized we were on a train, until we went around a corner, and he could see the rest of the train in front of us. Then he yelled in a loud voice "train, we're on a train"! It was a special moment to see him so excited! Tom and his girlfriend Jane, welcomed us and we decided to lay low, and not tell anyone we were in town, except for my folks. My mom and dad came over for dinner and a visit. It was so good to see them, and they really enjoyed us, and we enjoyed visiting with them. After a great visit we went to Seattle, boarded the train, and "chugged" back to Spokane. I had an overwhelming feeling that Litia was closing in on us. Daviduke said he had been in Arizona at a carnival, and thought it was a good place to move to. I wanted to leave, so we quit school. I talked Sharri into going with me, and the four of us headed out. Frog wasn't quite "potty trained" so it became my goal to train him. I got a party hat, and a party whistle. I kneeled next to Frog on the pot, about the time I figured he needed to go. As he sat there, I talked, and played with him until he did the deed. Then I put the hat on him and blew the party whistle. In short, I made an exciting event of it, and I only had to do this a few times before he got the idea, and started using the toilet on his own.

Daviduke knew some people in Lake Oswego, so we stopped there for a visit on our way to Arizona. They were nice people, and let us camp on their lawn overnight. They lived right on the lake, and we enjoyed the swimming and beer drinking with them.

I had a real scary moment, when Daviduke, Sharri, and I were drinking a beer while sunning at the end of the dock. Frog was playing in the sand at the head of the dock. I was keeping a pretty good eye on him, but somehow he had fallen off the first part of the dock without any of us seeing him. I finally noticed he was no longer in sight, and took off running down the dock. I spotted him laid on his back, looking up at me, on the bottom in about three feet of water. I jumped in and felt like I almost broke my leg on a rock sticking up; I grabbed my son and laid him face down on the dock. I started slapping his back, and he started coughing up water. He was all right! It was a close call, but I have never been so scared in my life. I shook for quite a while after that, knowing how close we came to disaster! The incident woke me up, and I vowed to be "much more careful" with my son. We loaded up and went down through Utah to Arizona. I could see this was going to be completely different from anything I had experienced before. When we entered Apache Junction we were all "taken" by the cactus and the Superstition Mountains in the background. We decided this was the place for us, and started looking for a house to rent in Apache Junction. We found an old one story kind of shabby place for cheap, right across from the dog track on Apache Way.

An Italian "mobster" looking guy named Geno owned the place. It had a swamp cooler on the house; a kind of "poor man's" air conditioning, so we knew it probably wouldn't get to awful uncomfortable there.

At first I had nothing to do, but I had "unemployment" coming in, so money wasn't an immediate problem, but we knew we would eventually have to make some money. Daviduke and I started "picking" the local dump. We salvaged everything we could, and Sharri sold the stuff at the rummage sale at the "dog track" on the weekend. We found a lot of drugs in the dump, because "snow birds" - people who came down for the winter - threw them out. We found a lot of speed, ludes, and downers of all types, that we were able to re-sell.

Eventually we started catching scorpions, rattlesnakes, and tarantulas for sale. A guy, a couple of houses over, bought scorpions for a dollar a piece from me. He made clear paper weights with a scorpion posturing inside. A.S.U bought the live rattlesnakes to milk for venom. I had a long reed out of the Suarro Cactus with a rope, and ring near the end, so it formed a noose, I could put over the snake, and pull tight. Then I dropped the snake into a gunny sack. They only paid twelve dollars each for them, and they were hard to find. It was dangerous because once a "rattler" rattling hard had tried to back me into one that was not rattling. I made the most money off of the scorpions, because they were easier to find. All I had to do was find an old lumber pile on the fringes of the desert. I usually got fifty to one hundred of them at a "pop". The only place I could find where there were a lot of tarantulas, was up at Canyon Lake, in the sand near the shore. I never found a great amount of them and only collected ten dollars each for them.

There was a "rock hound" nearby, and he said he would buy all the turquoise and apache tears I could find. I decided to "Expand my horizons" and start mining up in the Superstitions. I had picked up another dog, I also called "Louie the Licker". He was also a big German shepherd, who loved to hike the Superstitions with me. I found some turquoise and apache tears up there, and was able to make some money this way. The Superstition Mountains were an incredible place to hike. I think the cactus gardens are the best I have ever seen. We wore thick boots, and always had pliers in our back pockets because of cactus. Jumping cactus as well as others could only be easily pulled off with pliers.

Once Louie lagged behind and we could no longer see him, but I could hear him back a ways "whimpering". When we got to him he was standing on a rock, almost completely covered in jumping cactus balls. As I pulled them off with pliers, he whimpered on each one I pulled off. He got a lot wiser about walking in the desert after that experience.

As we were hiking up a dry wash one day, we climbed over a cliff on the side of the mountains, and there was an antelope laying on his side with his legs out in a defensive position. It had the side eaten out, and had a look of terror in its eyes. It had mummified and my guess was a puma had held it down and eaten the side out while it was still alive.

The Superstition Mountains were famous for the Lost Dutchman Gold Mine, which supposedly existed there. Seems an old Dutchman had found an incredulously good mine, and had died without telling anyone where it was at. When he died they found a large amount of gold under his bed, that he had mined.

There were guys all over those mountains looking for the "lost mine". I had someone shoot a warning shot near me once, when I was up there. There were also guys in the local taverns selling "bogus" maps of where the mine was. Of course if a person had a "real" map where the mine was, he would go locate the mine instead of selling the map for a hundred bucks. The maps usually have something like the soldier died here, the big cactus is here, the broken rock is here, and so - on and on! There was a little building near the road in front of our house. An old lady that constantly had a cigarette in her hand or mouth had made into a restaurant. Sharri started working as a waitress for her, so I only took drugs from the dump to make money for a time.

Daviduke moved on. He brought over a guy to drink with one night. Sharri, Frog and I went to bed, and this guy was deliberately making unnecessary noise, and when I got up to confront him, he got "pissy" with me about it, so I punched him out. Daviduke got an "attitude" about it, so he moved on. I didn't see him again until another "rock festival" in Washington a couple of years later. He eventually got "beat to death", because he tried to stop a fight between a couple of guys, when one turned on him, and killed him! It wasn't hard to believe something like that could happen to him. He was always trying to be the good guy and preach to people.

I was kind of a "fish out of water" here, and looked for ways to get wet. There was a pool at a motel a short ways away, and I got to "pool hop" now and then. I put my boy on my shoulders; told him to close his eyes, and hold his breath; then walked out on the diving board and dove off head first. Frog came up all excited, and I thought that was pretty "cool", he could do that.

About a mile away was a mine shaft, about twenty five meters wide, 150 meters deep that filled full of water. It had real cold water in it and was very refreshing on a hot day. Some days a guy with a "wrecker truck" would drive his wrecker to the high side above the pond, and stretch his cable with a pulley on it across to the lower side. I zipped across the pond and let go to fall about twenty feet into the water. I met a local guy that had buried a bus in the ground for a house. He put in a couple of periscope windows so he could see some views and get natural light down there. It worked very well, because it was always cool down there. Rattlers, scorpions, lizards, spiders, and other critters were getting in to enjoy the cool also. He always had to beat around with a stick, and inspect before he made himself at home when he went down there.

He turned me on to a "cool" thing to do. He heard about rain in the mountains above. We could grab some tubes and go out to a big wash in the desert and wait. When the "flash flood" came, a wall of water came down the wash. We just sat back in our tube and rode it for a while. The only drawback was "rattlers" and other critters got caught up in this water. They were also swimming in the wash. Then they were swept downstream. Needless to say, we had to watch what was in the water next to us.

Besides going all the way up to Canyon or Roosevelt lakes, there wasn't many wet things to do except float the Verde River. People could take a tube, and a cooler upstream, and float down. There were cliffs along the way to dive off. The first time I went, I cut the hell out of the bottom of my foot on the broken bottles that idiots had thrown in. Since then they have banned glass. I heard it is safer. There were irrigation canals, but the cops "busted" us for swimming in them.

Our landlord Geno had a 1962 Cadillac convertible he was selling - so I bought it. I got a set of bull horns about a meter wide, and mounted them on the hood of my white Cadillac. It looked pretty slick, and Sharri and I, with Frog, wore cowboy hats when we rode in the caddy.

Out on the desert I met a guy from Oregon who was hiking. Bob was just in the area for a few months for work. I liked the guy and sometimes we hiked together. One evening we went to Tortilla Flats in my car to do some drinking in a bar there. I don't know why we really went there, except we thought the name was "cool". The bar was at the end of a long building - the only building there. We got a few beers and Bob went to the rear to use the head. When he finally came back his head was all red, swollen, and a little bloody. He had gone out on a porch in the rear up against the desert, and taken his unit out to wiz. He fell over forward into a depression full of "jumping cactus". His face got the worst of it, and I had a good laugh at his swollen face. He was in misery the first few days, and didn't think it was so funny.

There was a canopy building place right next to my driveway leading to the road. One day the foreman came over to speak to me. Sharri walked down the driveway in a bikini, and she had a fabulous body. The foreman said "he wanted me to talk to her about walking down the driveway like that anymore". Some worker had stapled his hand because he was watching

Sharri walk by. I told him "I'd do what I could", but thought it was funny, and enjoyed watching her walk myself.

I knew a guy from home named Theo that lived in Phoenix. I was glad I lived in the junction when I got a smell of the air at Theo's. It was near stockyards in South Phoenix, and smelled terrible. We had a date with Theo and his wife to go to a concert at A.S.U. It was Arlo Guthrie and J.J. Cale. I hadn't realized how many great songs J.J. had written that other bands made famous like "Cocaine" and "They Call Me the Breeze". It was pretty good, and after we dropped Theo and his wife off at their place, Sharri and I continued down to Nogales. Nogales was pretty tame compared to Tijuana, but we stocked up on tequila anyway, since that was the only hard liquor we drank. The next concert we went to was the guitar player from early Fleetwood Mac named Bob Welch and Little Richard. Sharri and I both enjoyed this concert much more since it was in a small venue where we were expected to sit. This time Frog was with us. Everything went off without a hitch, and my son yelled, and clapped at the concert. Little Richard spotted him, and sat Frog on his piano when he played Tooty-Fruity. After the song he gave Frog one of his bracelets and Frog walked back beaming with joy. That was my son's first experience with live rock - but not his last.

The next and last time I saw Theo, he told me a story about losing almost twelve hundred dollars out of his pocket. He was on the way over to buy a new motorcycle, when his van over heated. He pulled over; got out; opened his hood; and gave it some water, and time to "cool off". He continued on, and when he got to the motorcycle shop, he reached in his front pocket, and the money was gone! He knew the only place he stopped was where his van over heated; so he went back to look. When he'd almost lost hope, he happened to spot his money hanging on a small bush. He got his new dirt bike, and he really liked tearing up the desert on his new bike.

One morning I heard a knock at the door, and when I opened it - there was Litia! She had tracked me down by my unemployment checks. I just invited her in, and when Sharri appeared, Litia got it all. I think she came down to see if we had any future, but when she saw Sharri she knew that wasn't so. She couldn't cause me any problems because I had proven I could keep Frog in good care. She slept on the couch and I kept Frog with me, so she couldn't sneak off with him that night. Early the next day she took off.

A guy up the road was selling a big 58 Chevy school bus. He had taken all the seats out and created a bedroom at the back of the bus. I bought it, and put a couple of couches up front. I put "Marrikech Express" on the destination sign above the windshield.

I wanted to go on the road with just Frog and not Sharri. We had a good half of a year, but it was getting very hot in Apache Junction, and I was wanting to be a bachelor again, so I took Sharri to the bus station and she left for Spokane. We decided to go to the south rim of the Grand Canyon, and off Frog and I went in our big bus with "Marrikech Express" on the destination sign.

CHAPTER 18

THE BIG HOLE

We headed up the long grade, leading to Flagstaff, and picked up hitch hikers on the way.

The first was a big guy named Bart. He had long blond hair, a walking stick, and was surprisingly soft spoken for a really big guy. I instantly liked the guy, and he also was heading up to the South Rim. I enjoyed his company all the way up. I picked up a few more people in Flag. One was a black girl, along with a couple of white guys, and I really wondered what their situation was. I soon found they were just friends.

She was always "hitting" on me, but I really wasn't interested. The only thing we ever did, was stand in front of the big Fred Harvey Grocery and kiss. There were a lot of old folks going in and out, and it "grossed" some of them out. We thought it was hilarious.

First thing when we got in the park I needed a long term parking situation. I met a black couple name "Raz" and "Liz". They lived there in a small cottage, because they worked there, and their employers provided the cottage. They let me put my bus in the driveway in front. They also had sixteen kids of all races, ages, and genders. One was "Little Raz", a black boy about four years old same age as my son. They had a good time playing together which gave me some time to investigate the Canyon some.

I needed work because my money was running low and got a "killer" job at a park on the way, just before the Grand Canyon Park. It was fashioned after the Flintstones. It was called "Bedrock", and my job was to watch Flintstones cartoons, and build what I saw. I built cars that looked like the foot powered Flintstone's cars. I built the wheels by putting chicken wire over fifty-five gallon drums, and covering them with mortar. I made them rough, and they looked like rocks. The frame was rough, burned wood, and an upholsterer made the "leopard skin" top. I also made televisions out of mortared chicken wire with big Flintstone posters in the screen.

Once I made a whole market full of goods, like big pterodactyl steaks made of wood rounds that were carved and painted. A record player made with log rings for records, and a carved bird with his beak as the needle. Giant axes, beds, canned goods etc., anything I saw on cartoons. All the buildings; that looked like caves, were already done, even the theatre. I had one of the buildings for a shop, and had three to six guys working for me.

It didn't pay a lot, only six dollars an hour. I could work as many hours as I wanted, so the money built up fairly quick. Liz, or one of her daughters watched Frog while I worked, and the company let me use the pick up to get back and forth to work. There were good and bad things about Raz, Liz, and his "family". Every time I walked into Raz's house there was music and dancing going on and they barbequed every night. Raz had moved his whole family from L.A. Some were his "blood kids";

and some he picked up along the way. A couple of his young adult sons, had scars on their chests and necks from knife fights in L.A. I heard Raz was fooling around with his step-daughter, especially one that appeared to be a sixteen year old Indian girl. He never "fessed-up" to anything when I asked him. Once I saw Raz chasing his sons down the street, shooting a pistol in the air.

His sons were fooling around with the "daughters" too! In the meantime Bart and I hung together a lot. There were a lot of young girls there that came to work in the commercial businesses. All the workers were put up in one section of the park that consisted of cottages, with pretty girls going from one cottage to another to party. There were always parties in the evening either at the cottages, or "keg parties" on the rim of the canyon. There were so many "available" women there I had one going out the back door of my bus, while another was coming in the front. Bart had his own place, so he was no problem.

Once Bart and I hiked all the way down to the bottom of the canyon. There is an old ranch down there, and we got some peyote' from some Indians I met. It tasted like "crap" and was a bit hard to "choke down", but it sure was hallucinogenic. I ate it a lot at work, and it seemed to make it easier to "create".

We were partying so much that sometimes I had no time for sleep, so I hid behind some plywood and slept on the job. I liked going to a club in Tuciana with two of Raz's sons. Those guys could really dance, and were showing me. I could never move as good as they could, but I got a few "moves" down because of them.

I heard that Jimi Hendrix was hanging with Mama Cass of the "Mamas and the Pappas". I couldn't figure out why Jimi would have dated Mama Cass except maybe he needed warmth in the winter and shade in the summer.

I also heard in a letter from my ma, that a friend had told her a story about a friend of mine named Butch. He had gone to "Lost Wages" with his super beautiful girlfriend. She was "stunning" but wore way too much makeup for my taste. Anyway they met the comedian Andy Kaufman and somehow had ended up partying with him. Evidently Kaufman wanted Butch's girlfriend and Butch ended up coming back to town alone. I heard about a year later she came back to Butch, because Kaufman had "dumped" her.

These were the days of the "Easy Rider" movie, Zap Magazines, R Crumbs weird cartoons, and the animated movie "Fritz the Cat", in which all the blacks were depicted as crows. Eventually I saw this funny movie at a theatre in Key West. These were great times for me, but I knew this adventure was about to end, because my job was "petering out" and a guy had stolen my bus. I stayed a couple of days down in Flag, with a "For Sale" sign on my bus, when a guy approached me about buying it. He gave me a hundred bucks to hold it a day for him, but that evening when I came back from a party in Flag, my bus was gone. I went to the cops, but could see they weren't going to do anything for this long haired "hippie".

I "pondered" my next move, and while "pondering", I heard the Apaches were selling off a pickup truck, that they no longer needed. I went to look at it, and the body was real sweet, but the motor was tired. It was a 58 Chevy truck with the wrap around rear window, and I knew it would get me to my next destination alright, but probably not much farther. I was thinking I wanted to go to Key West, as Bart had said "there could be work there", because of the lobster season.   Bart claimed he would come a little later.

I received the last of my pay and thanked the boss for the job. We went to Raz and Liz and bid everyone farewell. Frog and I drove east in our pickup.

We picked up hitchhikers and oil all the way there. The truck "slung" a lot of oil. We picked up guys and gals, so we had someone else to drive. I could stretch out in the pickup bed every once in a while. One of the girls was real cute, and stretched out with Frog and I. We were just kissing, and cuddling, but she felt good to Frog and me.

We went through New Mexico, Texas, Arkansas, Mississippi, Alabama, Tennessee, Georgia and Florida on the way to Key West. There were terrific lightning storms in the hills of New Mexico. Not much to see in Texas, but we thought the farmland of Arkansas was very green and pretty. We were impressed with the size of the Mississippi River when we crossed at Memphis. I forgot Louisiana, and only took notice when we went through where Tabasco sauce is made. I didn't see much of the other states, because I was either sleeping or didn't see much that impressed me.

I knew I was in for some "red neck attitude" the first place we stopped for fuel in Florida. My truck leaked a little radiator water and some "red neck" at the station started giving me "lip" about the damage it was doing to his asphalt. I dumped a little clean water on it and declared it was all right. Anyway we took notice of it and we moved on.

I was impressed with the length of the bridge going out to the Keys. Being a "water guy" it was good to get out of the dryness and into the wetness again and it was warm.

KEY WEST

After we crossed the bridge to Key West, we went straight to the water front. In the evening everyone went to the waterfront to watch the sun go down. We were cruising along the road on the water front, and it was like a festival going on. People everywhere talking, hanging, roller skating, fishing, picnics, playing music; people were having fun! About halfway down the street, just before it turned on to Duval Street, the main drag in Key West; the truck died. I opened the hood and the starter had fallen off, and was laying on the road, cables still attached. We rolled it off to the side, and I pondered the situation. We were not at all prepared for it. I had no tools with me at all. About then a guy walked over and asked if I had a clear title for it, and I said "yes". After he walked around inspecting it he offered to buy it right there. After a bit of discussion we settled on a decent price, and I gathered my son and stuff. He wanted it because the body was real fine since it came from the desert. Most vehicles had body rot even early on in their life, because Key West is so close to sea level. We bid farewell to the others that traveled there with me, and hung around there talking to locals. We needed a place to live pronto, and some people told me they lived at a place called the "Morrison Hotel", located in the middle of town on a side street. We stayed down at the dock until it started getting dark. Somehow we got a free meal that was offered to us. It was the first time we had eaten jambalaya along with the chicken and watermelon, we thought it was all good.

I finally set out with my pack on my back, and Frog with his little one on. The hotel was kind of "cool" looking, all white with green trim and a balcony along the front. The price was right, and the guy that bought my truck had given me cash, so we settled in. I figured if I didn't get more money, we had enough to stay about a month and a half.

Key West had a lot of coconut trees and the street out front was lined with them. It seemed very tropical. There were also key limes, bananas, mangos and citrus to be foraged. I never stole these items off the trees; instead I was very casual, and asked. Maybe because I had a little boy with me people usually let me help myself.

At first I couldn't find any work, but found I could sell key limes. I went up in the tree with a bucket with a rope attached and picked the limes. Then lowered the bucket to Frog who put them in boxes. The money was enough to keep us in food and a little more. Eventually my key lime supply dried up, as the season was over. We could only get enough other fruit for our consumption, but not enough to sell.

I got pretty chummy with some other young people, and of course we drank and smoked together! I met a girl named Janie that had come there from Indiana. She was average looking, and just a little on the skinny side. We got along well and soon she moved in with us. It really helped, because she had a job as a waitress at a popular place on Duval Street.

After a while we went to a prearranged meeting spot, where I was to meet Bart, so I could get in on the lobster season.

He never showed at the bar, nor had anyone seen him. I also found out the lobster season was really lousy that year, and I probably wouldn't get in on it anyway.

Just when things were really getting rough; I heard about a job on Stock Island, which was right across a short bridge from Key West. It was a construction laborer job, and right up my alley. If I'd had tools I probably could have gotten a job as a carpenter, as their "carpenters" weren't very talented and I felt I was. I would have gotten a lot better pay somewhere else, but we were good with what I got. It was a concrete, multi-story apartment building. Basically we poured a concrete floor, then block layers laid block walls, then we poured another concrete floor right on up. My job was to install, then pull plywood forms, without busting - up the plastic plumbing.

We were so desperate for money just before the job came up, I had sold my blood at the blood bank for fifteen dollars. I was saving my money because it was August, and the Keys get real hot and miserable from then on. I thought we'd leave before it got really bad.

There was a movie theatre on Duval Street that showed "Hipster" movies. They showed films like "Easy Rider", "Up in Smoke" and they were showing "Fritz the Cat" now. A bunch of us got all "smoked up" and went to see it. It was easy for me because Janie watched Frog. The movie was animated, and in a "Harlem" type setting with crows as blacks. It was funny, but pretty "dirty". We had a lot of fun with it, and it was a "Happening" in Key West right then.

Since it was getting so hot and miserable in Key West, we knew we wanted to leave soon, but I'd enjoyed my time there. We liked hanging out at the wharf in the evening, mingling, fishing, and watching the sun go down, but really the swimming there was the only relief from the heat. My hotel room only had a "swamp cooler" and no air conditioning. "Swamp coolers" were only partly effective.

On a weekend Frog and I got on a bus to Miami, to check it out and buy a car, with the money I had saved. We ended up at the park in Coconut Grove, but I realized early on it was just full of black guys looking to take advantage of others; so we got the heck out of there. We went to a section of town that had miles of car lots. After looking at cars for a few hours, I spied a 64 Rambler Wagon. I thought it could be good because we could sleep in the back, and it got good gas mileage to boot. It seemed to run good and I bought it after a test ride.

We drove up to Hollywood Florida, just north of Miami to find a girl I met in the Grand Canyon, named Dianne. After a lot of looking we finally found her, but things had changed, as she had a serious boyfriend by then. We hung with her a little while, then left back to Key West. On the way we did some swimming along the long bridge to stay cool. I noticed the car we bought wasn't staying very cool, and I had to stop for water a couple of times. When we got back to Key West, I got some radiator "clean out stuff" and it seemed to take care of the problem for now.

I talked to my boss and he let me stay in one of the semi-finished apartments on the job - so we moved out of the Morrison Hotel. This was about the time the Doors had done their LP "Morrison Hotel" so I thought it was "cool" we had stayed in the Morrison Hotel. Janie stayed in the room for a

while longer, until she finally moved in with friends. One
evening a clerk in a convenience store accused me of stealing.
I knew I hadn't, and told him to call the cops if he felt
confident. I wanted to be searched by the cops, so that the
clerk couldn't plant anything on me. He was just a "red neck"
starting trouble. When the cops searched me of course I didn't
have anything stolen, but they were also "red neck" and
wanted to escort this "long hair" off the island. I didn't want
to tell them we were living on my job sight, because I figured
it wasn't legal, and didn't want to make my boss or myself
"hot".   We got in my Rambler and drove off the island,
thinking they would follow us a short ways, then they'd turn
off, and we'd go back. But to my surprise they just stayed
behind me all the way to Pine Key. By that time it was pretty
dark, so we went to Pine Key Lake and slept in the back over
night. The next morning we jumped into the lake to cool off,
and noticed a lot of snapping turtles. Then I saw something
watching me! It was about a two meter alligator. He was
following me around, looking like he was stalking me. He
kept his distance, and I finished my swim. I wouldn't let Frog
get in the water, and it turned out to be a good story for my
friends when we got back.

Now it was not only very hot, but it rained a lot, and the
misery increased and I knew it was time to leave. We had saved
a bit of money since I didn't have to pay rent for a while.

Janie didn't like it when I said "I was going" because she
thought she was coming along. I told her that was not the case,
and said "goodbye" to her and my job. - Go West young man
I had to stay on top of the water in the car on the way back, but it
was easier and cheaper than all the oil in the truck on the way

over. We just slept in the back and didn't spend much time anywhere on the road at first. We stopped in Nashville and in New Orleans, but that was about all until El Paso. At El Paso I had to cross the border into Juarez. Juarez was huge. By far the biggest Mexican city I'd ever encountered to that point. Frog and I walked around Juarez looking at the sights until we eventually got off the "main drag" a bit.

We met Felix on a side street there. He was about my age, seemed like a good guy, and kinda showed us around. Usually I can tell by the people a person talks to what kind of person they are, and he turned out to be friendly - no threat! He introduced us to a few people, some family, and besides smoking his pot, we were also fed by his family. I speak some Spanish, left over from Spanish class in high school, so I get along with Mexicans pretty well. I have always insisted that I speak to Mexicans in Spanish, and they in English so we both get better at conversing. It was getting real late so after Felix, and his family gave Frog some presents, we headed for our car to cross the border. When we got to the border the guards asked me to step out of the car for a search. They searched the car, and of course found nothing; then they turned to me and asked me to empty my pockets. I did so, but when I got to my shirt pocket I felt a joint, and remembered Felix had put a joint in there for later. I tried to eat it, but three or four of them jumped on me and choked the mangled joint out of me. They immediately handcuffed me, and took me inside, and sat me down with Frog sitting on my lap. That's the second time that happened in my life! I didn't know what was going to happen and they left me there to sweat - it - out. Finally they took the handcuffs off and told me to step up to the counter. All my stuff out of my pocket, including the crumpled up joint, were laying there, and to my astonishment, he pushed everything into a big brown envelope, and said "we could leave". It was a close call, but when we got out of Texas, I straightened the joint, and smoked it in celebration. We decided to head back to Arizona, knowing we had Friends there!

CHAPTER 19

ARIZONA AGAIN

After we finally got through the bugs at Beaumont, Texas was pretty much clear sailing. The bugs of Beaumont were so thick I turned on my wipers so I could see. All I accomplished was to make my windshield blood from one side to the other. I had to stick my head out the window a ways, till I passed through them; then washed my windshield off, and on we went.

When we got back to Apache Junction, I only was able to find one girl I knew previously. Her name was Carol, and she was the former girlfriend of the guy that rented my old house after me. I knew them both because we lived on the front end of the property in my bus for a few weeks after they took possession of the house. We liked them both, and it was at least good to see one of them. We tried our hand at love at first, but soon decided we would rather be friends instead. I ran into my buddy that had the bus buried for a house, and found out the snakes, spiders, and bugs got to be too much, so he moved into an above-the-ground dwelling. He told me about a construction job pouring cement, and I got that job. It worked out well, because Carol said "she would watch Frog" while I worked, and the price was right. It was so hot we worked from ten or twelve at night, to six in the morning. Because of the heat and dryness we had very little time to "work" this "hot" mud.

We still had some money left but wanted to make a lot more. Since Carol let Frog and I live there cheap, I was able to save a lot.

She introduced me to a guy that lived in Mesa, named Brett. He was originally from Casa Grande, a place he always called "Kegger", I guess because he and his buds had a lot of keg parties there. He evidently kept the machines running at Spreckles Sugar, nearby. He had an alright apartment in Mesa, and he let us stay there sometimes. It was good to give Carol a break sometimes anyway.

Brett told me about a concert coming up at an outdoor venue. It was a place that made artificial surf, with big wave making machines. It was really "cool" as it had a big beach and guys surfing the waves. The band that was to play was called "Pink Floyd". I didn't know much about them except they had an album called "Mendelsom". This band turned out to be one of my favorites. Brett and I went to see them, and there was a good sized crowd on the beach, but looking back I can't believe there weren't more. They played Rock like we had never heard before, and we were both "blown away". Rodger Waters was really outstanding, but their guitar player David Gilmore was probably the best guitarist I'd ever seen. Of course we were really loaded on Tequila and weed, which even made it a better experience. Sid Barrett was great and died later at a young age. What a great place to see a great band. If I had to rate Rock - these guys would be on the top five, right along with the Stones, Beattles, The Who, and Led Zeppelin. We could see these guys weren't going to be any "one hit wonders". That night I formed a great bond with Brett that really paid off big time down the road!

SANTA - DON'T EAT THE BROWNIES!

Brett was a bachelor also and we spent a lot of time together in Tempe bars and parties looking for women. They were a little harder for Brett to get, as he was overweight, wore glasses and wasn't especially appealing looking. His selling point was his easy going nature. He asked me to go to "Kegger" with him to meet some of his friends. We ended up at a keg party down there, and it seemed kinda like the ones we had at home in Bennington. I met a lot of future friends, and two that stood out, were a couple of Mexican buds - Bobby and Vince. It really got my attention when Bobby said "he could sell me kilos of pot for $75 each, if I could buy a good sized amount". I thought about it and said "I could probably only buy fifteen at first, but would buy more each time". He said "he thought he could do that" for now.

We left, and when I asked Brett "if Bobby was just blowing smoke out of his ass", Brett said "he had connections and was for real"!

I thought about it hard for a few days, and decided the risk was worth it, and could do some things to minimize the risk. I told Brett to tell them I'd buy fifteen. It was Christmas and I was running out of steady work anyway.

CHAPTER 20

SMUGGLER

I had saved fifteen hundred dollars plus enough to get to Bennington in the old Rambler. We did the deal on the desert near "Kegger" and Frog and I left heading north! I decided to go over to the Grapevine in California and head right up I-5. Being the time of year it was, we did well, there was only a little snow in the Siskiyous. I put the kilos in a big plastic bag and put it where the spare would normally go. Then I put baby powder in and out of the bag, and all over back there. That stuff really neutralized the smell. Then we filled the whole back over the spare tire deck with clothes, and everything we had. It worked well as we made Bennington without a hitch - except for putting water in the wagon's radiator a few times. I learned to take a bunch of milk jugs full of water in the back. Even though the Rambler used a lot of water, I knew it was utterly reliable.

When we got to Bennington, we needed a place where there was no drug action, or other strife. My buddy Pete's place fit the bill, for a few days, while I got my bearings. He was working in the Yard, and we got along well with his wife Jill. He had a spare room they wanted to use for kids, but there was some sort of problem there. I never let them or anyone else know I had fifteen kilos of weed in my car, knowing "loose lips sink ships".

I needed a good place to put kilos in bulk, and my lake lot would fill the bill. No one lived close enough to see what I was doing. I set about digging a hole big enough to have a room underground with shelves, and a hatch that I could dig up without

too much trouble. I had to hand dig it, but it was fairly easy,
because it was compact sand. Except for the roof that was
buried, I didn't even have to shore it up much. I could get about
five or so pounds at a time out of it, and even had a scale. I
wanted to weigh and package it up in zips down there.   I sold it
for one hundred twenty five a pound, or we dickered on the price
for more, and I sold it very quick as it was good quality. Dealers
always wanted fluffy, dry pot, so they could add a little water
and make a lot of "lids" out of it, and this stuff fit the bill. So I
more than doubled my money, and the dealers almost doubled
theirs by the time it got to the consumer. We ran into my old
buddy Bill. He, Marvin, and Billy White Shoes were riding in an
old Lincoln limousine they bought somewhere cheap.

        He had an old phone in the rear seat that made Bill look
important when he was on it even though it didn't actually work.
Bill looked almost identical to Steve Stills, and he acted like he
was Steve Stills and we of course told the chicks he was. You
wouldn't believe how many times that got him women. We
were heavily into the blues then, and we went to Seattle in that
"Cool" car to see a guy named Johnnie Shines. It was in an old
place up past the Paramount Theatre a little ways. The owners
thought the place was too small, so they rented the adjoining
place and just knocked a hole in the wall literally so the
customers could use the other half. They had tables and chairs,
but evidently didn't have time to clean up the sheetrock on the
floor, because it was scattered everywhere. We didn't care
anymore than anyone else, as Johnnie really shined that night.
What a stroke of luck finding a tight act like this in a literal hole-
in-the-wall. We spent all our money, and barely had enough to

get gas to get back, but what a good welcome back by my buds
who were looking to buy!

I didn't give Pete or Jill a clue as to what I was doing,
because I never let anyone call there about business. I took those
kind of calls at Rod's house.

Like I said, I sold it quick and doubled my money, and
then some. Frog and I set out to Arizona again, after I gave Pete
a bullshit story, why we were leaving so soon. I decided to go
down I - 5 to the Columbia River and turn left toward Northern
Utah. We only had to go through the Blue Mountains, and the
snow was starting to go away. When we got to Utah and headed
south, the snow was light, dry powder, very easy to navigate.
Not much to report until we got to Salt Lake City, when I heard
on the radio that the Moody Blues were to play that evening at
the Salt Palace. We didn't have enough money to get to Arizona
and get Frog and I into the concert, but I managed to talk a ticket
taker into letting us both in on my ticket. What a good concert
and Frog recognized some of the songs from the radio. He was
thoroughly happy, and clapped, and smiled so hard I thought he
would split his head from ear to ear. It was a good time without
any drink or pot, because I never smoked or drank when I was
smuggling, and I wanted to enjoy it with my son to the fullest.
Of course the band finished up with a long version of "Tuesday
Afternoon", then came out for more after the place went "nuts".
They had so many good songs, they easily filled the evening
with great songs.

We finally had to leave, and not much happened till we
got near Page, Arizona - Navajo Country! We noticed all the
mounds in the purple dirt. When we stopped in Page at a

convenience store, I saw an Indian guy there that looked like he wanted to talk to me. I asked him about the mounds, and he told me they were "Hogans", and he lived in one. After introducing myself, he told me he was called Spud, cause he was sort of short - in fact real short, probably around five foot. He was a very nice guy from what I'd heard so far, and asked "if we wanted to come over and check out his "Hogan". I agreed, and we followed him over to his place. I was surprised at how nice it was inside. He had no electricity, but he had lights and a stereo record player that worked off his truck battery. I wondered why he opened his hood when we got there, and hooked a couple of wires from his "Hogan" to the battery. He even had a couple of windows built into it, and it was finely decorated throughout with Navajo and Mexican blankets and such.

After a while he pulled out a couple of "joints". I asked, "since it was getting dark if later we could "crash there" and he happily said" why sure". I told him "I didn't like to smoke when I was driving", so since Frog and I could "crash" there later I smoked and listened to tunes. "Spud" was real envious when he found out we had just seen the Moody Blues. After a while, we were just worn out, and true to his word "Spud" had a nice place set up in the corner for us, complete with Navajo and Mexican blankets. Frog and I went out like a light. About five in the morning we got up and said goodbye to "Spud", and promised him we would return sometime - unfortunately a promise we would not keep, and off we went to Brett's.

Brett agreed he would charge me ten dollars for every kilo I bought through him, and that he would let it ride until I was through smuggling, and get it in one lump sum. I thought that was a great deal, and we hardly got settled into Brett's apartment before he said "Bobby is ready to do a deal". I told him to tell Bobby I could get thirty kilos this time. That made him happier, but he still wanted me to buy much more. I heard they were able to get the "weed" across the border in an old car that had the front fenders fully sealed. They loaded up the fenders by taking the headlights out. They got about seventy five kilos in there. I guess they were going through some small border crossing two or three times a week. We did the deal again in the desert. After saying "Goodbye" to everyone, we pulled out. This time I decided to go across Hoover Dam and up through Vegas, Reno, and across to Shasta California then up I - 5. We were able to drive right across Hoover Dam, a feat you cannot accomplish now after 911 happened. We got us a ninety nine cent breakfast in Vegas on our way. From there just monotonous driving until we hit Fallon Nevada. I went a little fast through town and got pulled over. The cop said "We had to go with him to see the judge, and pay the fine since I was a visitor there." Frog and I started to walk to his car, when he said "aren't you going to lock it up"? Just in case he suspected anything I said "No, we don't have anything worth stealing anyway", and we got in the back of his car. The judge - a woman, fined me forty nine dollars; I paid it and the cop took us back to our wagon. We said "see yah", and drove out of town north. I learned a lesson, and never sped through any "dink" towns after that.

When we got to Susanville California - the gateway to the high altitude Lassater Forest, we waited till a snowplow came through, and followed him to Shasta. Nothing much more happened until we reached the Cowlitz River in Washington.

We noticed a bunch of guys in waders like I'd seen before in the river. We pulled up to see they were dipping smelt, a small edible fish. One guy offered me some, because they were getting a bunch every dip. He gave me a bucket about a quarter of the way full. I'd eaten smelt before and they were pretty good, but when we got to Pete's we cooked some up and they were terrible, no flavor, so we threw the rest into the compost. The ones I'd had before, Pete and I dipped from the salt water. We learned to always get them from out of the saltwater. No wonder the guy was happy to give me a bunch of these crappy fish!

I got my mom to watch Frog, and Pete, Jill, and I went out to a bar to do some dancing.

CROSS-EYED MARY

I was doing the "potato" around the dance floor with a girl, when I noticed a cute blond, with a great body, going out of her way to make eye contact with me. The next song I strolled over and asked her to dance, which she excitedly accepted. I noticed although she was a ten in all departments, she was cross-eyed as hell. At first it was hard to not notice, but after a while we were having a good old time, and I didn't notice anymore. During the next band break, we went out to a friend's car, and toasted a dooby. I used this opportunity to cop a "feel", and later we went to her house, and we were on from then on. She asked me a couple of days later to move in to her basement apartment, and I did. I'll bet the old landlady above got a good earful because Mary was a noisy one at night. I took the old Rambler out to the lake, and unloaded it, came back to Mary's and put my car in the garage, and she let me use her Volvo. I discretely started getting rid of the dope. I didn't even let Mary know what I was doing. I didn't share her phone number with any of the dealers. Once again I was getting rid of it pretty fast. Mary wanted to get tickets to see Yoko One at the Paramount in Seattle, but I talked her out of it. When John Lennon died Yoko thought she could sing. She was screechy, and terrible. Turned out they cancelled the show, because they couldn't sell any tickets. People had heard how lousy she sang.   However there was another rock festival about to happen in Washington called the Satsop River Fair. It was to feature Eric Burden and War, Delaney and Bonnie, The Range Hoods, and a bunch of good Seattle bands. Mary had to work and couldn't go, so I went with a very funny black guy named Terry. We walked right up the road and into the gate, and no one was collecting money - it was free! When we got by the river, people were forging the river up to their necks, with packs on their heads. They probably felt kind of dumb when we told them they didn't have to sneak in, as they weren't collecting any money at the main gate anyway.

Terry found about seven hundred reds on the ground, which we didn't want because neither one of us liked downers, but they were great for trading for stuff we did like.

I noticed my old buds Jake the nut, Homo, Rick Weltman, Dan, Jimmy, and a whole bunch of others from Bennington were there in an old 1940 Chev. Bus they managed to get running. This old bus was nicknamed the "Nickle Grabber", because it was used to cross the old bridge in Bennington in the old days, and cost a nickel. Those guys were having big time fun with that thing at the festival. They all called themselves the Butthead Brothers, or something like that. Duane was there with his brother Leonard; seemed like half the guys I knew were there.

We didn't know much about Delaney and Bonnie, but we really liked Eric Burden and War, and I wasn't disappointed. On one of the first days a guy had brought a big truck full of watermelons and parked it right down in front, next to the stage. He thought he would make a killing selling them but the crowd of broke, hungry hippies had other ideas. They, myself included, jumped up on the sides of the truck, and started throwing melons to people. First the guy started throwing mud at us to try to get us to stop. That didn't work, so he got in the truck and drove right into the middle of the crowd in front of the stage. One girl got her legs broken before the crowd drug him out of the truck and stopped the truck there. The rest of the watermelons were given to the crowd, and the truck was moved off. We don't know what happened to the driver, but I don't think it was pretty. Leonard was wearing a pair of world war two flying goggles, and he and a drunk girl stumbled up on the stage, hitting microphone wires, and mics flew everywhere. They got to the last microphone standing, and yelled some unintelligible words. It was funny only because of his goggles and both of them being so stumbling drunk.

Another day the bikers, who always caused trouble at the festivals, started trying to rape women. Everyone grabbed shovels, axes, hammers, whatever we could get, and attacked them. They were definitely wanting to leave, when one of the bikers decided he wanted to start shooting. One guy got shot in the arm, and the bikers left. The festivals usually went well, everything except the bikers.

We found the "Bean Lady" and she was our only source of nourishment as usual.

The local bands filled up the four days of fun, and we were sad to leave when it was over - back to reality!

When I got back I found out from a friend the Wineburger Distillery had closed and sold the rest of their stock to the Carcheesy Brothers who changed the wine a little and sold it under a different name. This was significant to me because I was able to buy right from the Winery in the past. They had good tall bottle wine with foil on the top, I could get for seventy five cents a bottle in bulk, and two fifty for a gallon in bulk. Once when I bought five hundred bottles, Jimmy and I took them to a big party in the Cascade Mountains. This was one of those parties where someone showed up with a big flatbed truck and a generator, and bands came to play out in the middle of nowhere. We knew there would be hundreds of people there. It was a long haul up a dirt road and very steep on one side. Jimmy and I sampled too much of our wine on the way up, and woke up in my van next to a big bank, with the rear doors wide open and all the wine gone. We shook it off, and drove up the rest of the way to find Bill had unloaded it and was already selling it. I had bought mescaline real cheap, and had to step on it, and cap it; but I was able to sell a bottle of wine, and a hit of mescaline for a total of one dollar. Because of me, there were a lot of high hippies there.

On another occasion, I bought two hundred gallons of Wineburger wine and Daviduke and I drove it over to a party

that was to happen just over the mountains in Eastern
Washington. It was in an empty section of the desert. All was
well until Daviduke started running his mouth to the bikers about
all the wine we had. Pretty soon there were a lot of bikers
hanging around our van. We got the idea they were going to
take it all. I grabbed Daviduke, threw him in the van and we
"hauled ass". A couple of bikes tried to chase us down the dirt
road, but I kicked up a lot of dust and they gave it up soon.
When we got back to town, Homo showed me the pictures he
took of one of our trips to Alaska firefighting, when we pulled
the door off the cabin in the woods, thinking we could stay there;
and new pictures of the Satsop River Fair. There was one of me
sitting on the throne in the outhouse, but the best of all pics was
one of Leonard with his WWII flying goggles on, leaning on a
drunk chick on the stage at Satsop. I only had to sell a couple of
days, and my stash was gone. In the meantime I met a guy - Sam
by way of a real good old buddy I could trust. I needed to buy as
much pot as I could to keep my connection happy, and Sam
expressed interest in riding along, and scoring fifty kilos of his
own. That would mean we could score 170 kilos, and I knew
Bobby would like that, so I told Sam O.K. Sam was kinda a
heavy set guy; looked a little rough around the edges, but was
easy to talk too.

Sam, Frog, and I took off and headed south on I-5.
Everything went well until we got to Shasta, ready to cross over
to Susanville. My Rambler didn't sound real good, but it never
did, and I knew it could make it all right. There was a surprise
snow storm between us and Susanville, and my plan was to
follow a snowplow there. Sam decided my old wagon wasn't
going to make it, so Sam bailed out, and said "He would take a

bus back to Bennington". We bid him "farewell" and of course
we got to Mesa - no problem. His loss!

This time I had to wait awhile to score. We liked having
some time with Brett and Carol. I tried to set the two up, but
Carol was having no part of it, so they remained just friends.
Brett had bought this Chevy Vega new, and it was a real piece of
crap. He was complaining how he couldn't sell it for what he
owed on it. So we took a little trip up in the hills on back roads
by Payson. We stopped to look over a view, and Brett forgot to
put the E-brake on, and left it in neutral running. Just after he
got out, it rolled away right off a cliff. We could still see a little
of the grill sticking up because it hit the only rock sticking out of
the cliff, and stopped. We had to hitchhike back to Tempe, and
Brett looked a little shell - shocked. At least he didn't have that
piece of crap anymore.

We hung with my buddies and did some hiking up at my
old stomping grounds - the Superstition Mountains. There was
an old ghost town near the base, where they occasionally made
movies. I found a real old license plate in the junk pile there. I
also found lots of scorpions in the pile, but wasn't collecting
them to sell anymore. We were just killing time, until I could
score, and just when I was starting to get real impatient - Brett
said "we were ready".

We did the deal on the desert again near "Kegger",
except Bobby had sent a guy up to the only hill around to see if
any cops were up there with binoculars. Seems the cops were
known lately to watch from up there, the only vantage point
around, for suspicious activity on the desert. Everything was

copasetic and I scored 125 kilos this time. I picked up Frog at
Carols and we went north again.

This time we went to Page Arizona and up through Utah
to Idaho, Oregon, and across Washington to Bennington. I
always tried to go a different way so no one got used to seeing
me and got suspicious.

Mary and I caught up on things after I had stopped at the
lake and buried my load in my underground room. The first
night back was really good, but the second kinda weird. Mary
had invited her ex-husband Darrell over and another guy Dave,
neither of whom I had ever met before. Though I didn't know
them, I knew something about them. Mary's ex-husband Darrell
had to go in the military just after they got married. I heard that
Dave, Darrell's best friend, went right over and started banging
Mary. I don't think Darrell ever knew, and none of them knew, I
knew about it. It was hard for me to fathom Dave and Mary
there straight-faced. I didn't figure I would ever really trust
Mary much, and was real glad I didn't tell her what I was really
doing. I told her I was working in Arizona, but coming to
Bennington because my Mom was ill, and that didn't end up
being far from the truth.

I LOVE YOU DAD

One day my dad keeled over, and fell out of his boat in
the carport and died of a massive heart attack. He died almost
instantly, and none of us knew he even had heart problems. He
was always a smoker, but he also always got a physical. He had
our family doctor fooled I guess. Of course my mom took it real
hard, as he was the love of her life. My little brother Chopper

took it hard, but since my two older brothers Matt and Jan hadn't lived with my dad for a long time it wasn't quite so hard. We all especially appreciated my dad, because he had given my mom such a good life.

It was taking a bit of time to sell off my last load. The area was a little saturated with pot at that time.

We wanted to get my mom's mind off her woes, so I set about getting my mom to buy a fixer-upper house the three of us could work on for resale. We did so and bought a small house that had been used as a rental previously. It was pretty rough and had a complete used V-8 motor in the closet. It was tiny and needed a bigger front room, so we decided to remodel, and add on. It sorta worked except my mom broke down and cried often. Seemed like I did all the work, but we managed to sell it for a little profit, and it had kept my mom somewhat busy. Mary, Gregamo, Racoombs, Dave and I did some drinking over at Gregamos house, known as "the cliff house". We got to know Gregamo and his wife Ann well, as Gregamo would be my employee later on. As we were sitting around drinking, smoking, and listening to tunes, I noticed Dave's right heel was all rounded off. He was a cab driver and just his right heel was rounded because of the gas pedal. I realized I could tell a "Cabby" by his right heel from then on.

The next night I was out with Bill, Marvin, and Duane. We really had nothing planned, so we went over to "Mama Lowes" house. She was a fat, unattractive woman who frequented sailors. We were looking to raise hell, and really had no interest in her. We got pretty "loose" and took some of her Christmas presents in the bathroom unnoticed. We carefully opened the wrapping paper, and the end of the boxes within, and crapped in each. We carefully wrapped each back up, and put them back under the tree. She definitely couldn't say "she didn't get shit for Christmas"! She had a mighty surprise when she opened her presents.

We were kinda known for "trashing" houses. Besides crapping here or there, or having food fights, sometimes we would "shiskabob" anyone who was passed out, by rubbing catsup, mustard, or mayonnaise all over them. If everyone was passed out, sometimes we'd collect all the empty bottles and put them in the dryer; turn it on, then leave. Once Racoombs put a heater up against Steve's ass, and covered his eyes with peanut butter, when he was passed out. Steve woke up to a blistered ass, and thought he'd gone blind. Luckily no one really carried a grudge, especially if it was funny and bazaar. I finally got rid of the rest of my load, and decided to return. This time I left my Frog with my mom, because she really needed company. She really loved her grandson. I missed him because I was working hard on his education during those long rides. We kept a bunch of books in the car for him. I couldn't get him to sound out words well, but he could really memorize them. He got fairly good at math, spelling, and reading. It turned out he really needed the head start because he was just an average student later.

This time when I left, I moved out of Mary's also. She had changed, and we both agreed to it. We really enjoyed her, but it was time to move on.

I went down I-5 to the Grapevine and east to Mesa, because there was a lot of snowy conditions on the other routes.

This time the old Rambler wasn't running well and I wasn't sure I could trust it. I decided it was time to get a better "ride".

When I got to Brett's, there was a budding guitar player there, named Mickey. He expressed interest in my old wagon, because at that time he was on the move, playing his guitar, and could sleep in the wagon. I told him I would sell it to him cheap after I found a new "ride". I instantly liked Mickey, and thought he looked a lot like Burt Reynolds. He was real funny, and just out for fun. He had grown up in Mesa and when he was seventeen his mom turned him in for growing pot in the yard. He had done some wild things, such as stealing a safe with his friend Tom. When they couldn't get it open, they got cold feet and dumped it into the same five hundred foot deep mine shaft in Apache Junction that had filled with water; that we used to swim in.

I set about finding a good car to replace the old Rambler. I found a very clean, good looking 64 Chev long Station Wagon. It had a small V-8 and ran great. What I really liked was the huge amount of room under the rear bed. I had to have a ride I could stash two hundred fifty kilos in, and with the spare tire out and a little alteration it would just do it.

Brett told me that during a deal on the desert Bobby had been "ripped off" by two guys that pulled badges and guns, and said "they were cops". They really weren't, and it was just a scam to rip them off. I started thinking I didn't want to smuggle much longer because it was getting so dangerous. We did our deal in a different spot in the desert, and I bought two hundred fifty kilos. I was just barely able to hide it all in the car, but I managed to fill the back full of clothes, furniture, and junk.

Besides all the baby powder, the weather was cool and that really kept any smell away. I also had my wallet with a Washington Driver's License in a safe - box near Portland. I exchanged wallets with my one from Arizona on the way back. I thought if I got popped in Arizona with my load, I probably wouldn't do hard time. My license and plate were from Arizona, and I had no record in Arizona; but I did in Washington. During those times the States weren't communicating with each other so well.

It was such a pleasure driving my new "ride". I made it back to Bennington with ease. After I put away my load, I went to my mom's house, and found her in a little better spirits, because of Frog. My mom told me that "my little brother was kinda getting out of control". He was driving now, and had passed out in the middle of the only road going down to my Moms on the point. Cars had to drive around him Sunday morning to go to church. I looked in his ride, and found beer cans up to the back seat, and little pot plants growing out of his cars carpet in the passenger corner. It was beer - soaked and I guess he had dropped some "roaches" there with pot seeds in them and it started to grow. Anyway I didn't say a lot about it to him; because I felt who was I to say? I just told him to "be more careful". We stayed at my mom's for a couple of days. I could do some good there spending time with my mom. Now, with a good amount of money at hand, as I sold off my load, I wanted to build a house at the lake. I needed a foundation first and my buddy Bill, and I ended up partying with a guy we called "Donde" because he looked just like the kid from the comic strip. He knew how to lay blocks, and after we laid a footing down, he showed me how to do it. It was a "Piece of cake", and soon we had it done.

Frog and I moved into a little place on the east side of town with a black guy, I met through Marvin. We called him Montana, though I don't know why? He was a heavy set guy; wore glasses, and was not particularly good looking. We both shared the same kind of music, love of women and a need to party. He hung with us white guys mostly, but when we ran into black guys he knew, he acted like he didn't know me - kinda odd I thought but something I experienced before. There was a girl across the street that caught my eye, and evidently she noticed me. I knew about Penny because she had pursued her boyfriend Billy White Shoes, who was also the father of at least one of her kids, to extremism. He had to lay low in a different state for a long time. Evidently that time of her life was over, and she was a pretty, well built, available woman. It didn't take me long to start hanging at her house. She had three kids, but it had not taken much of a toll on her body, except as she always said "my tits are shot". It was a good set up for me. I liked "hanging" with her, but it was never going to go beyond that, so I slipped other chicks in here and there.

I bought a lumber package, and kept building my house. Besides Frog, selling my load and Penny I became very busy. This load went fairly quick because the county was pretty "dry". Brett, Bobby, and Vince decided to bring me a couple hundred kilos to sell for them while they stayed with me. I was able to sell most of it fast, but they had to leave some with me. I sent them the money later. While they were there, a friend of Penny's that I went to school with, wanted Bobby. So I set him up. She had a beautiful body, and Bobby was real happy for at least a couple of nights. Soon they had to leave, and life went back to "normal".

Logins and Messina was scheduled to open for the J. Giels band in Seattle at The Edmonson Arena, a nine thousand person venue. Both Montana and I couldn't wait to go. Logins and Messina were of course famous for their song "Your Mama don't dance, and your Daddy can't rock and roll". We went to see J. Giels Band mostly. We loved their "killer" album "Full House". We enjoyed Loggins and Messina, but when J. Giels came on, the place went nuts! They played Magic Dick's, "Wammer Jammer", "First I look in the purse", an old Isley Brothers redo, and "take out your false teeth mama, I want to suck on your gums". There was not a sole in the place that wasn't dancing and "rockin". The drummer tossed two sets of drumsticks into the crowd, and two of them fell into my hands. We were worn out when we left there from all the high energy music. After that, I carried that album around with me to parties. It was almost impossible to find another album to put on afterward, as it was so high energy. Every other album sounded dull.

I saw J. Giels open a few years later for the Rolling Stones, and they were still great. The singer Peter Wolf had the "Cool" moves, and put Mick Jaeger to shame dancing.

A week or so later I got some real distressing news; Bobby had been murdered, and they found him in the trunk of his own car. I knew at that point the dealing business had gotten way too dangerous. I didn't have a connection any longer anyway.

DEALING WITH DICK

I wanted to make one last big load. I found out from a friend that an old buddy, Dick Rappaport, was living in Tuscon and I could score from him. We stopped in Mesa to see Brett, and see if he'd agree to wait a little longer for his payoff, and he agreed. Also Mickey wanted to go, and ride up to Washington with me after the deal.

Dick lived in a suburb in a slump block house, in a middle class neighborhood. After a night of partying on the town, we made a deal. I didn't like it much because I thought it didn't look good at all to have us coming out the back door of Dick's place with big black bags full of kilos. I got about two hundred fifty kilos, and was a bit nervous heading out of Tucson. I was glad I didn't take Frog this time. Dick's girlfriend tried to put the bite on me when we were alone for about an hour, and I didn't bite. When Dick got back, he asked me "Did you screw my girlfriend"? Of course I set him straight, and he must have been getting used to that kind of crap coming from her, because he just forgot about it, and we remained good friends. In fact I set Brett up with Dick so he could score, and instead of me paying Brett ten dollars a kilo to score, he was now paying me. We took the load back and dropped Mickey off at Gregamo's house and went to the lake to put my load underground.

I always tried to be extra careful dealing. If I went to someone's house to deliver some pounds, I put the pounds in the customer's garbage can on the way in. Then if all looked good I went back out and got it. I kept just a few pounds, maybe five, above ground at a time.

I almost got popped, purely by accident, in Bennington.
I was at an out - of - the way convenience store getting a beer.
When I walked out of the store two cops, one I recognized, came
up to me on either side. The cop I knew Jim Johnson told me "I
was suspect in an earlier robbery attempt. I said "Look Jim I
haven't even been here earlier tonight, and you know me I've
only been arrested for drinking and fighting charges". He asked
me to step in the door and have the clerk take another look. Of
course she was mistaken and I walked away, but if the cops
would have searched my car, they would have found five pounds
of weed in my trunk!

I went to a sealed bid auction the school district had the
next day. There was a Dodge Sedan, fins, black, and with
"Official use only" printed on the side. I bid one hundred dollars
and to my surprise got it.

We wanted to take a road trip down south to see my
buddies. Mickey was back down there for now. Brett was still
there, but contemplating quitting his job. Karen, Dianne,
Montana, and I got in my black Dodge with the "Official use
only" on the side and left town. I was hanging with Karen, a girl
I knew by way of Litia. She loved to laugh, and was very pretty
with a great body. Dianne Let Montana know straight on she
was not interested in him, and when we got to Brett's, she let
him know she was not interested in him either.

We picked up Mickey and headed down to Tucson to see
Dick, as we were all friends of his by now. We went out on the
town to party and started shooting bottle rockets out of the
windows. We never got busted, thank God. We said our
"goodbyes" the next morning and headed back north. Somehow

on our way back up north I ended up with Dianne. She was also
a looker. I didn't mind, although I didn't know for sure if Karen
did.

When we got to Oregon, a "state bull" stopped us, and
when I asked why he just said "he wanted to see who was
inside". It seemed kinda dumb to me because it was an old car
that no one "official" would be riding in. While we were in
Mesa I paid Brett his money. He had about 5 thousand coming.
He promptly went out and bought a new 750 Honda. I hoped he
wouldn't kill himself on it. A mutual friend of ours in Arizona
had killed himself, when he hit a dead steer laying in the road at
about eighty miles per hour.

When we got back Karen, Dianne, and I went to the
Paramount Theatre in Seattle to see Three Dog Night opening for
Joe Cocker. Montana wasn't interested, especially since he
wasn't going to get anywhere with either of the girls.

Three Dog Night was hot at the time, and so was Joe
Cocker. I think Three Dog Night were the best singers I had
ever heard in a band. When Joe Cocker came on he looked like a
"spaz" up there, contorting and flailing around. We saw him
puke off the side of the stage at least once, but when it came his
time to get to the microphone, and sing, he was right on and
sounded great in spite of his intoxication.

We stopped at "Pig Alley", a tav in the Pike Street
Market, and had some beers. The girls had never been there
before, and the place was known for great blues artists just
coming in off the street, and playing. We heard some good blues
then headed back across the pond. Soon Dianne and Penny were

both done with me, because they figured out they weren't going to get anywhere with me.

I went out to a party with Bill and Barry Gutler, at a girl named Sid's house. I got close to her pretty quickly. She had a good body and was fun to be around, but she had the funniest breasts I had ever seen. They stuck out but they were small. Barry Gutler must have seen them before because he called her "midget tits". She had a son about the same age as Frog though. She eventually asked if we wanted to move in, and since we had moved out of the house we shared with Montana in East Bennington, I said "sure".

Her running water had sulfur in it, and more than once, I saw someone with a hangover, stick their face under the faucet, and get a big dose of rotten egg smell. It was enough to "gag a maggot". It was all pretty good there, because I was working on my house, selling off my approximately five hundred pounds of pot, and partying down with Sid. Frog was happy having Jed to play with, but he was almost school age. I had to get serious and make a more permanent life for us.

One morning after a party I woke up on the couch. Soon Sid and a guy I just met came downstairs from her bedroom together. I had been replaced. It was really alright because my house on the lake was finished enough to move Frog and I into. She was just a short term squeeze anyway that remained a good friend.

CHAPTER 21

LIFE ON THE LAKE

I got Frog in Kindergarten and sold most of my load, and finished my house.

In the spring Mickey came up on a 450 Honda. He was wearing a wetsuit under an old suit. I had a new fiberglass septic tank I hadn't put in the ground yet, and Mickey and I liked to play music in it. I had taken up the harmonica, and he still played good guitar.

My neighbor, a young good looking stud, with a pretty little wife, and small boy, were building their house at the same time. We met early on when Mickey and I were growing some big pot plants, disguised on the lot next to Dubs. He had discovered them and being a good old boy had left them alone, except to rave how good they looked.

Dirty Ned, Allan, Jon Sanyo, and Skip moved in a short ways away, and were reportedly trying to grow Opium Poppies. They were really the first hippies in town, and still doing bazaar things like growing poppies.

When it started getting near the next Christmas, I came up with a good plan. I rented a twenty four foot U-Haul truck and went out to a Christmas Tree Company, I had worked for, way back when, with Homo. I bought as many loose Christmas Trees, for a dollar a piece, as I could get in the truck. Brett was to be my partner, but Mickey rode down to Mesa with me to sell them. We found a vacant lot near Apache Junction on Apache Way. Mickey was a great salesman, and with Brett and I, sold all we had easily for a dollar a foot. Mickey got a dollar each, and made a lot of money too. The trees kind of sold themselves, because when we opened the back of the truck, there was still snow in back, and the evergreen smell filled the air for a few blocks around. We held up trees for customers to look at, and Mickey played his guitar as we sold. Once he held up a tree that had no limbs on one side, and when the customer complained about it, Mickey said "you don't have to buy a stand with this one, you can just nail it to the wall". The guy bought it! Sometimes we held a nice tree up with one hand, and a dog in the other, and half the time the customer bought the doggy one. Go figure! I took Frog with me, and Carol was happy to watch him while we sold trees.

When Brett and I split up the money, we had done really well. Mickey stayed in Mesa. I got a suit case, and got another connection to sell me about fifteen kilos. Frog and I took a bus back from Phoenix. While I was in line with Frog, with the big suitcase, a guy came up behind me that I was sure was a plainclothes cop. I wanted to throw him off, so I asked him if he'd watch my suitcase while I took my little boy to the bathroom. When we came out the suitcase was still there, and the guy was gone. It had worked!

I sold the pot when we returned and turned about twelve hundred dollars into about thirty five hundred dollars. It was a great way to increase the money we made off the Christmas tree sales. Brett made the same deal as me. We liked busing back home instead of driving. Especially since all the routes heading north were snowed in.

It felt good to be back home. This was my mom's first Christmas without my dad, and my brothers and I did what we could to ease her pain. My dad's mom had died a few years before my dad, and I didn't miss her at all. She gave my younger brother thousands of dollars' worth of things for Christmas, because he was her blood grandson, and give me and my older brothers something shitty, like a fruit cake. It was a bit humiliating, but I got her good one Christmas. I got a fruitcake, tore it in half, and let it get hard as a brick. Then I did the worst wrapping job I could do, and wrote her name on it. When she opened it in front of the family, she did the best she could, to be casual about it, but my older brothers, and I just "cracked up". My older brothers really got some respect for me since I had made a statement to her about her rudeness.

CHAPTER 22

WORKIN FOR A LIVING

I was no longer a smuggler, so I had to make a living somehow. Since I had done concrete work in the Seabees, I knew I could make a living at it. I hired Montana first, and made a good living at flatwork and walls. Montana eventually got lazy, and quit, so I hired Gregamo. He drank a lot, but did pretty good work, and wouldn't leave me hanging. Sometimes flatwork doesn't always dry on time, and we were stuck working on it till late at night. Gregamo always stuck it out with me. Sometimes Gregamo was hung over, and when he puked he just troweled it in. We also laid block, and could really bring in the bucks, because we were so fast.

I also had a pool of part time guys if I had a big job. Mickey was one of them when he was around. He came up with the novel idea of wearing old suits when we poured mud. We thought sometimes the customer looked out the window and thought, look at those clowns. We always did good work so we had a good laugh in the end and made money. I ran into a girl named Donna Crenshaw that I had met before. She was the girlfriend of one of my buddies by the lake. She was one of the prettiest girls I had ever seen. Brunette, good build, and just always looking to laugh. We started dating and progressed from there. She worked as a bartender at a place on the waterfront, and rented a good little house next to a creek where it emptied into the bay. After some good times dating, we decided we wanted to be around each other more, so we moved into her house. She liked Frog and Frog liked her, so we had a good time together.

One evening Gregamo and Ann came over looking white as a sheet. Greg and Ann lived down below a street in town, and Ann went outside to take the garbage out, and saw a sock laying in the bushes. She went over to pick it up, and discovered it was a dead body. She shrieked and Gregamo came out, and confirmed - yes it was on a dead body! They called the cops, and when the cop came he at first tried to tell them it was a manikin, and someone was trying to play a trick on them. Greg insisted he look again, and when the cop realized it was indeed a dead body he told Gregamo to take his wife in the house. Kinda dumb because she was the one who found it so she had already seen it. Anyway someone had hit - and run a pedestrian on the road above them, and was thrown to their yard below in the bushes. We spent a few hours comforting them, and settling them down before they went home.

Gregamo, and I went to work the next day, and he seemed to have regained his composure. After our work that day, Gregamo wanted to stop by a store and pick up some Rainier beer. That's all he drank, and he drank a lot. Dale Dawson was at the store, and told me a good story. His brother Tim was nicknamed "Elmer" for some reason, and their Dad's name was Elmer. A friend of Tim's called his house, and asked for Elmer. His Dad thinking it was for him said "Hello", and the kid asked him if he had any "Lids" for sale. Elmer said "What"? By then the damage was done, and Tim caught hell from his Dad.

Litia, my ex-wife, never even called to talk to Frog. I felt sorry for him, since I could tell it bothered him. Litia was still in town, and was on her second daughter out of wedlock, with a guy I sort of knew. It seemed like he just came around to knock her up, then he'd disappear again. The screwin you got, is the screwin you get because he finally had to pay her big money for child support. The two daughters had my last name, because she had never changed her name, but she did name Lonnie as the girl's dad.

I did Christmas trees again, but with Mickey this time. We took my ¾ ton Chevy down with a trailer behind it, both packed as full of Christmas trees as possible.

I wanted to set up in one spot on Apache Way, and Mickey wanted to set up a ways off the main drag. I did all right, though I didn't make as much as I did the first time. Mickey had a hard time, and really only sold enough to make his money back. Of course I bought kilos with the money to take back, and so did Mickey, but he couldn't get as much as me. We dropped off the U-Haul trailer, and off we went by way of Vegas, and Reno. When we got to Reno, I discovered I had lost all my traveling money somewhere, and Mickey didn't have any to start with. We stood in front of a casino and started "pan Handling". People really weren't giving us money, but were giving us coupons for a free drink and five dollars to gamble with, so we took turns using these coupons. We did that for a while and didn't get "squat" for money, until I "pan handled" an old guy, with a beautiful blond on each arm. He didn't give me any money, but there was a limo waiting for him, and after they got in, he sent one of the bimbos back with twenty silver dollars for me. When he didn't give me any money at first, I said "Can't afford it huh"? I think that comment is what got me the money!

That was enough money to buy the rest of our gas to get us home. We tuned in a good radio station on the way that was playing tunes like "They call me the Breeze" by Skynyrd. Leonard Skynard was very hot right then.

A couple of nights later Micky, Kevin, and I ended up with a couple of pretty girls, riding around with us in Kevin's car. I liked the looks of Gwen, as she had a great body. She had a lot of attention from guys, and I knew she wouldn't pay any attention to me, unless I did something unforgettable. She wanted to go home, so I got Kevin to stop by a store and I bought a pie. When I came back I managed to keep it hidden in the car. When we got to her house I slipped it under my shirt, and when we got to the door, and she puckered up for a kiss, I smashed that pie right in her face. Then I took off leaving her surprised and pie faced. It must have worked because she tracked me down and kept me company for the next couple months.

During those next couple of months, Mickey and I took Gwen, and another girl - a friend of mine, Victoria to Seattle, to a club where U-2 was playing. These two girls were elevens on the scale, and had sexy dresses on with high heels. They both looked very good and they knew it. After thoroughly enjoying the club, especially the music, we were pretty loose and ready to leave. We had taken the ferry over to Seattle, and walked a few blocks up to the club. So now, we were going to walk the few blocks back to the ferry. Victoria lost her high heel right in the middle of a major intersection, and fell on her butt. There she was struggling to get her heels back on, the cars honking, the drivers whistling and yelling sexual comments. We enjoyed the show and Gwen was looking good trying to help Victoria get to her feet. I think those two were right in their element, and enjoyed showing off and the spectators had certainly enjoyed the show.

Seattle was a reasonably safe musical place. Mickey, and I would take our guitars, and harps with us, and jam on the buses and street corners.

I started working for a construction company across the bay. I worked about six months for them, and when the job was over wanted to go somewhere warmer for a holiday. My good buddy Racooms wanted to join me.

We decided on Mazatlan Mexico. A lot of people really talked up Mazatlan, but after we got there, we weren't so keen on the place. We knew there was better. After a little skirmish at Senior Frogs, in which we were kicked out for being too rowdy, we managed to lock the door on the way out, and told everyone trying to go in, that it was closed. After a while the bouncers came out, and made us leave. It was a real dirty town. We sat on the wall on the waterfront walkway, and saw rats running in and out of the restaurants kitchen door. We couldn't wait to get out of there and on to "greener pastures".

Unfortunately it was Semana Santa or Easter, and everyone in Mexico goes somewhere on a trip. Subsequently all transportation was booked solid. We tried cars, buses, and boats, and all we could find was third class train seats to Guatalajara. We took the train, and rode with people, and farm animals in smelly cars all the way to Guatalajara. We were drinking lots of tequila, and that was the only positive, except of course getting out of Mazatlan. When we got to town we met a guy that was teaching Mexicans English. He was a great guy, and he put us up for a day or two. I think he was from Texas, and just wanted to have a bit of American company. We realized quickly that this wasn't our sort of place either, and decided to take a bus to Puerto Vallarta. It was just a few days until both our birthdays, and we stopped at Tequila Mexico to celebrate. There are twenty eight brands of tequila made there, including Quervo and Sauza. I wanted to tour some of these distilleries, so we got a bag of limes, and started at Quervo. This place let us drink lots of tequila during the tour. We went to the next place, and about halfway through the tour I told the tour lady in my best Spanish, "She didn't need to stick with us, and we could continue alone". To my amazement she took off. We ended up in a room with a swimming pool looking thing full of clear tequila. We were getting pretty "High" by now, and after we closed the big doors and locked them, we were just kinda lounging around the edge of the pool with our limes, and some cups we found - drinking. After a while the workers started pounding on the big doors yelling "Chinky Loco Americanos - Obierto"! We finally did, and they escorted us to the street.

The next place we went into was the Sauza Distillery. They just let us walk around that one. We met a guy named Jesus, one of the workers there, and had some laughs. Eventually we ended up in a room full of wooden casks. All of them had a date on them and there were three guys whose sole job was to put a hose from this portable pump into these casks. After they knocked the bungs out of them they pumped the tequila into a four inch pipe, sticking out of the floor.

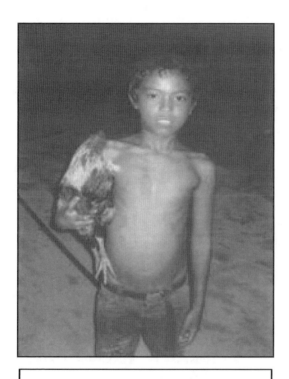

His Prized Possession

Tequila is made there, but bottled in Guatalajara, so that four inch pipe went to tanker trucks headed for Guatalajara. We started drinking with these guys, and after they got pretty wasted, Racooms and I were doing their job pumping out casks. Finally a boss came down and made us leave. So we're sitting on the corner back to back with what's left of our limes, because we are so drunk we're holding each other up that way.

Next I hear "Amigos" coming from a tanker truck. We look, and its' Jesus driving; the guy we just met earlier. He asked if "we wanted to ride with him to Guatalajara", and though that was the wrong direction' we jumped in. We had good conversation with Jesus all the way. There was a little faucet near the end of the tanker that we used to keep our tequila jug full. By the time we got to Guatalajara, we could barely stand.

MEETING POINT - PUNTA DE MITA

After a small altercation with some Mexican guys, we made our way back to Tim the teacher's apartment. The next morning we caught a bus, and headed out again for Puerto Vallarta. Even with a severe hangover the tamales they sell on the buses at the stops, were excellent.

Semani Santo was over and Mexico settled down a bit. We finally arrived in Vallarta, and we instantly liked it better than Mazatlan. It is fairly jungled in Vallarta, and was evidently the shooting location for a big movie "Night of the Iguana". We bought a watermelon and cut one end out of it, ate some of the pulp, and munched up the rest, so as it looked like watermelon soup inside. Then we poured in a bottle of tequila, a liter of orange juice, and filled what room was left with ice. The final treatment was just a dash of Tabasco and a couple of straws. We stood on the corner and drank this concoction, and offered some to others till it was near gone. When we offered it to an older American guy, he said, "I know where you want to be - Punta de Mita". I asked him about it, and he claimed it was a good place for young guys like us, and there were some things going on there. We continued to finish our concoction with help from others.

About then a guy pulled up in a Volkswagon van. He was obviously not Mexican, and neither were the other two guys with him. We asked him if he knew where Punta de Mita was, and he said "he lived there, and he would give us a ride there". After we introduced ourselves, he said his name was "Iguana", and that he was an "Aussie". He claimed he went up to San Diego for a few months to work, then come back to Punta de Mita, to live. I guess he could only stay in Mexico six months at a time on his visa so he returned to the states to renew. He had a pretty nice place on the side of the hill overlooking the Pacific Ocean. He had leveled an area out front and had paved it with these golf ball sized corals, which made it pretty sweet looking. He had a hammock to sleep in - one inside, and one outside. There was a Tienda nearby, and at night he ate at a local's house. Seems the locals had a community meal at one or another local's house, and anyone could pay a small sum, and eat there. That's what Racooms and I did, and ate our other meals out of what we could get from the Tienda.

As far as a place to live goes, we met a guy named Juan, who had a little outdoor bar on the beach. He was a real nice guy, and was married, and had twelve kids. He let us use a Palappa, right on the beach. It was basically a palm roof with three palm sides, which were previously used for people to change in before swimming. We hung our hammocks in there, we bought from a vender walking the beach. They were very good, and after we bargained for them they were also reasonable. We learned that the monument at the end of the road was called Punta de Mita (Meeting Point), and that the fishing village below was called "Corrales".

There was the beach and an apron of palm trees, then a bank, and a desert plateau above that - quite unique! There was decent snorkeling out front, and sometimes surf. It just happened there was good surf right then, and Iguana had boards for rent cheap. We both got one nearly every day there was good waves, and really had a blast! I even got pretty good at it.

Down the way a little toward Corrales, there was a good snorkeling spot, because it was protected by rocks and was calm. The water was somewhat discolored, as is the case in most of the Pacific in upper Mexico. I had a good set of fins, and mask, and a Hawaiian sling lance. It wasn't long before I was able to get us fresh fish for dinner. The rocks helped me in this endeavor. I could get a school of fish caught between myself and the rocks, and give them fake moves, one way or the other, and get them confused. When they were running in to each other, I'd shoot one.

We had no good way to cook them, but we also worked that out. There was a brothel, bar, restaurant combination on the beach nearby. If we got enough fish for a cook named Rosa, and us, she would cook it with the Aroz (rice) we gave her, and fresh vegis, and bring over the three plates of food in the evening. The three of us, ate at my Palappa. Rosa was kinda chubby, and not much to talk to, but these meals were way better than the community meals, that were usually potato, corn soup, tortillas, or something of that nature. Rosa just liked to hear us speak English, which was the case many times in Mexico. Sometimes guys bought us a beer in a bar just to get an English lesson. I spoke Spanish, and they would speak English, and we corrected each other, making the conversations beneficial to both of us. There was a big problem with flies here, especially in the shade. We believed the flies were caused by garbage, and human waste left in the open. We fashioned a rake and raked my Palappa and surrounding area up, and then did Juan's area over at the bar. We dug a hole and buried all the garbage and waste. Almost instantly the fly population was cut way down. Juan noticed, and I told him "No basura - no moscoes", which means no garbage - no flies roughly translated. To my satisfaction he started raking, and burying. It was much more pleasant to sit at his bar after he started doing this. This one act made our section of beach the most pristine around.

One particular day the waves were especially good. Racooms, Iguana, and I got boards and headed to our beach. Iguana was an especially good surfer. Racooms, and I were just intermediate, but I was able to handle the overhead cleanups, but Racooms couldn't. We had so much fun that day. I was able to use medium sized boards now and that made it even more fun. I was "goofy foot" and liked right breaks more than left breaks. That means I had to look over my right shoulder to see the wave, but still enjoyed it. Sometimes I could catch a left break and face the wave, although there was mostly right breaks here.

Iguana was so smooth. He was a real pleasure to watch, and a mentor.

On a down surf day, Racooms and I decided to go to a place called Yelapa. We had to hitch a ride to Vallarta, and leave on a ferry from there. With Tequila and limes in hand, we boarded. Tequila was so cheap, we drank it all the time because it was our favorite anyway. Yelapa was an Island, or an end to a peninsula that stuck out in the sea; we never found out which it was. When we pulled in we were impressed by the beautiful turquoise color of the cove, and the jungle surrounding it. We took a horseback ride up the hill where we could really see the place well. The horse I rode had one eye gone, so I felt sorry for the poor steed. I wondered how it could have lost an eye.

There were young boys around with Iguanas on leashes, some up to two meters long. For a few pesos a tourist could take pictures with these big lizards. Once an iguana ran into the thatch roof of our Palappa, and a bunch of boys came running through trying to catch it - now I see why. It was an economic opportunity for the boy who caught it. We did some snorkeling, then jumped on the boat to go back. As we were about to board, we met a relocated American guy, who claimed he lived with a Mexican girl there, and had done so for about four months. He seemed pretty happy, and he said "he had really learned Spanish well, by living with her".

When we got to Vallarta, we got another bottle of tequila, and some limes, and contemplated getting back to Punta de Mita. We drank awhile before we started hitch - hiking. It was hard to get rides so close to town, and the buses were all over-flowing at that time of day. It was a nice day so we just walked for a while. We went by a huge banana plantation, and spied a good sling of bananas. Temptation got the better of me, and I cut down, and put the sling in my knap sack. We gorged ourselves on them for a while, because they were the small pocitos we called them - also known as apple bananas. We ate about half of the delicious fruit right there.

Finally we managed to get a bus to Xuantacastle, a suburb of Vallarta. From there we started hitch-hiking again. About halfway there we got a ride in the back of a pickup with some local boys. We had a good time talking to them about the surf that had been up lately.

After we got out, I had my thumb out to get the rest of our ride to our Palappa. Racooms was passed out by now in the concrete gutter on the side of the road. I finally got us a ride, and helped Racooms stagger to his feet and into the car. Juan was our provider and took us straight to our Palappa, where we both passed out.

As a reader you might be wondering how my "bud" got the name Racooms. His real name was similar to that, but he had a habit of going into a bar, and picking a fight with the baddest guy in the bar. Since he was a lousy fighter, he usually got two black eyes, therefore for a few days he resembled a raccoon.

The local fisherman had a sunken, open fishing boat they were trying to pull up on the beach to repair. They had a truck tied to the bow and Fishermen lining the sides trying to pull it up. Racooms, and I wanted to help, so I grabbed the rim of the boat too. Racooms grabbed the rope from the truck, and just as we were about to tell him not to grab the rope; it snapped. It dammed near pulled his arm off and he spent the rest of the trip in pain.

We finally said "goodbye" to Iguana, Juan, Rosa, and some of the others there including an American guy known by the locals as "Monkey Surfer". He would pump and jump up and down on his board as he surfed. I saw him and his girlfriend on the next trip there as well.

Nothing really happened out of the ordinary on the plane trip back, except the new departure tax took us by surprise, and we barely had enough pesos to get out of the country. We were distressed about the tax but soon almost every country was doing it.

When I got back I went over to my mom's, and got Frog. I was relieved to see that my mom was getting closer to her old self, thanks to the positive effect of Frog. We went over to Donna's, and we were both happy to see each other. I of course had a lot of good stories for her and everyone else and so did Racooms.

We went to a party out near the canal, and a very pretty blond who seemed to have everything came on to me. She looked great, except she was a little bit slumping in the shoulders. She had great "Hooters", and if she would have corrected her slumping shoulders, they would have been spectacular. After a lot of smoking, and drinking, I had a weak moment, and stayed the night with her. I felt kinda bad about it, and a day or so later, Donna ran into Linda in a store, and when they started talking Linda said "she was seeing Joe", and Donna said "well I am seeing Joe", so that was the end of both of them for me.

Gregamo said "he wanted to take a scuba diving course. We thought it would be right down my alley, to do the same. So we both took the same course from the same locally famous instructor. Larry not only taught scuba diving, but also had a wet suit company. He was a great instructor. We bought great wet suits from Larry. His house had a pool, so we spent time in the water perfecting our skills. We were required to learn a lot, including dive tables, and safety. It felt good to be taught by such a capable diver, and diving would become a big part of my life. Though it was referred to as "cold water diving", we bought great wet suits from Larry, and it was fairly comfortable in Puget Sound.

Puget Sound, and the nearby waters are a meca for divers, and were labeled by Jaques Cousteu, as one of the best five places in the world to dive. We also found some great spots to snorkel.

Gregamo, and I started diving quite a lot, but Gregamo drank a lot of beer, and I told him "I would not dive with him when he had been doing a lot of drinking". His brother Racooms sometimes dove with us which would later prove to be deadly! I went to a club with Gregamo, and Racooms on Saturday night. Sometimes just for fun I wore two different shoes like a work boot and a tennis shoe. No one ever really noticed prompting me to say "don't spend a lot of money on footwear, because no one will notice it". I noticed a curly dark haired, Italian looking girl, who Racooms seemed to know. He introduced us, and we went about having a great evening dancing and laughing. Finally at the end of the night, she noticed my shoes and got a good laugh. I must have looked like a clown with my strap overalls on, and two different shoes. She left with her friend, and went home.

I wanted to see more of her, and Racooms told me right where she lived. She lived near the canal with her ten year old son. I went over one evening and drank a little wine, and sat with her. She was very happy to see me, and so was I to see her. Maria's son was in bed, and asleep by then. I started putting the moves on her, and "copping" some feels on the couch with her. To my surprise she said "you know I have a bed". She didn't have to tell me twice, and from that point on we were an item. I met her son Gabe the next time over, and immediately liked him. She was just freshly separated, and once I accompanied her over to her estranged husband's house to drop off Gabe. I could tell her estranged husband didn't like her and me together. I was waiting in the car for her, and could hear them arguing. She was a real knockout, and I could understand why he didn't want to lose her.

My daughter Fawn was in harm's way. Her mom, an absolute eleven on the scale, and I had dated and lived together for a couple of years, but had never married. During the years after my daughter's birth, I paid child support, remodeled her home to make it bigger, and had my daughter on every other weekend, and holidays, somewhat more in the summer. Her mom, and I had just grown apart, and I lived in a house on a lake while she, and my daughter lived at her house, near the canal. It was kind of a heart-breaking situation for me, because it was sometimes hard for me to get to see my Fawn.

A guy was living with Fawn's mom that was going berserk on drugs. He chopped up the house, and threatened my Fawn. I went over there, and confronted him just as the Sheriffs were there to take him away. I wanted Fawn's mom, to let me take her to my house to live. Since she loved her daughter so, she agreed Fawn would have a better life with me, and agreed to let her stay with me. Fawn was torn but finally came with me.

Frog was in his own place by now. We had built him a little house on a piece of property I owned. So there was just Fawn, and I in my little house on Tahuyeh. I was so happy to have her with me, it was a dream come true. We took some steps right away to help her fit in. I knew some Indian people that had a daughter about the same age, and arranged to have them hang together. Also my brother Chopper was married and had three boys, two of whom were about Fawn's age. She had to change schools and so on, but her new friends helped a lot.

I took her and Frog to Maui with me on vacation, to get her mind off the change, and help us get "tighter". We had a good time snorkeling, hanging on the beach, and exploring. We stayed in Paia, one of my favorite towns on earth. Paia is a little town that is kind of a melting pot of locals, tourists, windsurfers, surfers, and others. I had been to Paia before, and had many adventures there. It was hard to get my daughter into it. She was sad to leave her Mom's house, but I had to protect my daughter. I don't think her heart was completely in the trip. She thought pineapples grew on trees until we got there - at least now she knows they are the fruit of a plant.

When we got back I kept up with Maria. She wanted to live together, so we moved into her house. We rented my little house on the lake to a bachelor that really liked living there. I liked living at Marias but my daughter wasn't completely into it. She was real shy, and Maria didn't do anything to endear herself to Fawn. I enjoyed Gabe and he was kinda my little buddy.

Van Halen was coming to Seattle and Maria, T, Junior and I went. We borrowed a paraplegic van, and wheelchair from a friend. We filled brand new piss bags with whiskey, so it looked just like piss, and strapped them to the side of the wheelchair. Junior decided he would play the part of the paraplegic in the chair. He really looked the part with just white socks on his feet, and kind of a withdrawn look. We pulled up next to the venue, and the girls rolled him out of the van; I went to park the van. When I returned we all rolled him in, and the cops didn't even give us a second look. The crowd was sympathetic and let me roll Junior right up to the front. They were really rockin hard. Junior was getting tired of sitting in that wheelchair, surrounded by people standing and jamming.

Between songs I told Junior to stand up. He didn't want to at first, but we talked him into it. Then I announced to the crowd loudly that "it was a miracle, Van Halen made him walk again"! Everyone laughed. We folded the chair, we drank the whiskey and enjoyed the rest of the show.

Maria wanted to go on a trip with me, so we decided on French Polynesia. It would be fairly expensive, and be a long plane ride, but we decided to split costs and go. Because French Polynesia was expensive, I got her to agree to try to camp, and stay at cheaper places when possible. We went for two weeks, and suffered through about an eighteen hour flight there and back. When we got to Bora Bora we thought it was all worth it. It was so pretty. Speaking of pretty, Maria was just that in the new bathing suit she bought especially for the trip. I made her a halter top out of a coconut that was really great looking on her. Bora Bora is an island surrounded by a coral ring, with a very green mountain that you never forget once you've seen it. Its' very easy going, and the French Juandarms there have very little to do. Besides snorkeling in the lagoon, created by the coral outer ring, we were able to rent a Bateu (boat) with a small motor, for fishing and exploring. We were all set up for rough camping, complete with a queen blow up mattress. We stayed one night on the outer island, which is part of the coral ring. We had a plastic tarp for a roof; our blow up air mattress, a couple of sheets and hand fashioned pillows. We were laying out very comfortable, when a feral pig stuck his head in right next to Marias, and started grunting. She was so scared she screamed, and I thought she was going right through that tarp. That was the end of the camping.

On Sunday the local women put on the wildest, most colorful dresses I'd ever seen, and went to the local church. We thought it was kind of a show for the tourists. We took bikes around the island and talked a farmer out of some of his fresh vegetables. We managed to cook those and a barracuda I caught out of the Bateu. That was one of the best meals we had on Bora Bora.

Maria wanted to explore other islands, so we went to Rangaroa - a less visited island than Bora Bora. We managed to get a little place right on the water for fifty dollars a night. That was my kinda place, for a great price. It was owned by a jolly, fat local, and her skinny little husband. He played the concertina, and she sang on their patio next to us. She was so jolly when she laughed her big tits fell out of her moo-moo dress, and she just put them back in. This made her laugh even harder, and her little husband and I joined in.

There was pretty good snorkeling around the island on the leeward side. It was only good for three days of excitement when we got the urge to explore the other islands. So we moved on.

Our next move was to an Island that was connected to another by a bridge called Huahini iti and Hui. Iti means small, and Hui means big. We explored both but stayed on Huahini Iti. Maria was getting to me. She wanted to stay in a resort that cost two hundred eighty a night. I could have done better but she wasn't hearing of it. The Frenchman that ran the place - Noel, was a great guy, and even took me diving with him. That was my only time diving in French Polynesia, as it was pretty mediocre. We did get some bugs (lobster) and he let me use his kitchen to cook that, and the vegetables we schemed. If we walked up to the nearby road when we heard the horn honk, we could get a fresh French bread about six in the morning. I wondered what all the long mailbox looking boxes were and found out this truck delivered fresh French bread every day to those boxes. We also had one of those great fresh French breads with the meal.

One evening some of the locals put on a hula show. I'd seen some shows before in Hawaii, but the Tahitians put them to shame. I could see why these dances were meant to promote sex, because when that show was over, I had a "woodie". There was one particular girl in that show that caught my eye! She was a beautiful Tahitian, who could really move. She worked in the restaurant in the resort during the day. In my conversations with her, she told me she also spoke Spanish. So when Maria and I ate there I was flirting with her in Spanish saying she was very pretty and so on right in front of Maria. I knew Maria didn't understand, but thought she was getting the drift of things. I really didn't care because she was forcing me to spend so much money I didn't have.

Noel told me some of the little huts weren't finished yet, and knowing I was a carpenter, wanted me to stay awhile, and finish them. He said he would "handle the visa" and "pay me a wage", as well as give me one of the huts to live in. The only drawback was an infection that had attacked the whole staff's eyes, except the beauty from the Hula show. I feared if I took him up on the offer I would get it next. Their eyes were terribly inflamed, and looked like hell. I shouldn't have let that stop me. I should have sent Maria home and stayed a few months. I normally took advantage of those kind of adventurous situations. Instead we booked on a cheap freighter cruising to Tahiti. I used a can line to fish, and had two of them out off the back of the ship. The crew couldn't figure out what I was doing until one of my lines started ripping out and about an eight kilo tuna started jumping on my line. I wouldn't get it in because the freighter was "booking" pretty fast. I knew they wouldn't stop for me. Still, it was fun to play until it broke off. It was quite beautiful cruising on that old ship; past Morea, and on to Tahiti. The biggest town on Tahiti is Papeete, a town of about one hundred thousand inhabitants. We pulled in at about midnight, and just got a place there for the night. It wasn't cheap, as nothing is in French Polynesia, compared to the U.S. The next day we got a rental car, and set out to tour the island. We drove by a military base, and said "Howdy" to Pierce, a young French Military guy that had a place next to us on Huihini - iti. He was a pleasant young guy, we drank some beers with, and thoroughly enjoyed.

We continued on, and came to a pretty, natural pool I recognized from the first Mutiny on the Bounty movie. There was some good surf nearby, but I just was never able to get a board together, and we were leaving the next day. Those islands had more coconut and banana trees on them than any I'd ever seen before.

There were a lot of land owners drying coconuts for copra. They have big sliding racks, and the sun cooks the oil out of it, and it drips into a catch basin. They make skin and tanning lotions out of the copra. After a long flight back Maria, and I settled into a somewhat shaky relationship. She drank a lot of wine in the evening, and that combined with her cutting me off, was getting to me.

Brett had a new Cadillac, and was driving around selling kilos, he was scoring from my connection Dick. Mickey said "Brett had gotten busted, and was in a low-security prison". I always thought he was showing off a bit too much, and wasn't careful. This situation proved I was right!

I was doing a good amount of salmon fishing up at Neah Bay with my buddies. Neah Bay is the most Northwest tip of the U.S. The rock formations are stunningly beautiful there. My buddy and former neighbor, Wart, Racooms, and I took a small twelve foot boat with two medium sized motors, up there fishing. We flew out the six miles to get there, jumping wave to wave. Both Wart, and Racooms had control of a motor. We got our fish, and had a hairy ride back. I'll never forget the look on their faces as they controlled those motors.

On another trip Wart, Racooms, Gregamo, Mickey and I rented a kicker boat, with a small outboard on it. When we got in to start it, it didn't run as good as the boat next to it, so we changed boats. We were at another place farther down the coast called La Push. It was a fishing resort on an Indian reservation, up a river a ways. We cruised out next to a charter boat, and we were "hammering" the fish, and the charter boat was not. We were deliberately talking real loud about all our fish, and we could hear people on the charter boat complaining about the lack of fish. We were getting a mixture of big king, and silver salmon. When we came back to the dock some guy with kids came down the dock. The guy said "we used their motor". When he said that Wart just pushed him out of the way and said "It ran real good", and we left. I guess the motor was his own and not a rental motor. Oh well!

Three Stooges?

A couple of days later Racooms and I decided to go diving in the morning. The night before I partied with Racooms, but my plan was not to let him party very late. I wanted him to be sharp in the morning, as diving is dangerous, and a diver should be sharp. He had a tendency to drink too much, like his brother Gregamo, so I tried to curb his drinking that night. We partied till about eleven then I dropped him off at his place. We got our stuff together, and went to Agate Pass Bridge the next morning. There are a couple of big concrete pilings in about fifteen meters of water there and we wanted to dive them because we knew there were fish there.

We got our gear together, suited up then walked down to the beach, and into the water. The current was just slowly moving, because the tide was slack. The sun was out and it looked like a fine day to dive. I couldn't help but notice how clouded the water was. Racooms was right behind me as I started to swim the twenty five meters to the east of the pilings. I got out to the piling and put my mask up on my forehead, and just relaxed there, to wait for my buddy. When I turned to him, he had started to swim towards shore. I yelled, "whats up Racooms"? He just took his mask off, and said "my heads screwed up"! He rolled over in about two or three meters of water, and I couldn't see him anymore!

CHAPTER 23

MEXICO AGAIN

Work was getting slow where I was working as a carpenter, building apartment houses. It was time to go to Mexico again. We had so much fun the first trip to Punta de Mita I wanted to go back.

I flew down to Vallarta and hitch hiked out to Punta de Mita. This time there was a Canadian couple in the van that went out there reasonably cheap. Burl and Vicky were just dating, but came to find some space together here. I told them about my Palappa on the beach, and said I had room if they had hammocks. Turned out a vendor came by, and they both scored. Three hammocks in there looked like bats in a cave. It was pretty comfortable, and we could get the whole Palappa "Rocking" when we were swinging.

Burl was a real sensible, good guy. Fun to hang with, and we got a lot of snorkeling, beach combing, and partying in. We even did a lot of coconut bowling. Vicky was nice and pleasing to the eyes. She loved to take her top off and hang on the beach topless for hours. We didn't mind, as no red blooded American man would.

I had to get more fish, so we'd all have fish to eat. I enlisted Burl's help for that, by getting him to kinda corral the fish into my spot, where I could get them up against a big rock, and get them confused. We had a good week together. A guy told me to go to Mantachin Bay near San Blas if I wanted to get some good surf.

Iguana wasn't here right now, because of some visa problems. I grabbed a board from under Iguana's pad on the way out. I had to go to Tepic, and to the ocean from there. I left Burl and Vicky at the Palappa and saw them no more on that trip. Mantachin Bay is known as having the longest wave in the northern hemisphere. A surfer could catch a wave at Mantachin Bay and ride it seven minutes, all the way to Santa Fe. It's a long mushy ride though. I stayed at the point that's called La Islita. I managed to hitch all the way to La Islita, my final destination as it turned out.

I started walking down the beach to the Palappas on the point. There was a real happy looking guy headed towards me with an immediate handshake. He called himself Gorge. I introduced myself and really felt friendly toward him right away. He seemed real friendly.

I asked him "If I could rent the Palappa" that sat on the point, and he said he was renting the whole compound, that also included a restaurant. He said "he would rent it to me for a ridiculous sum of ten dollars". I couldn't believe I had the best place and it even had screens to keep the "skeeters" away. This place was a step up, because it had big openings with screens therefore a great view of the surf. I needed screens because the mosquitoes were everywhere, along with fireflies, that glowed at night. It looked like a bunch of Christmas lights flying around. Even the Palappa didn't keep them all out at night. I had to smolder coconut husks in my Palappa. I collected old cocos during the day, and lay them out in the dirt road, out back. The cars, and small trucks shredded the husks enough so that I

"Moons Out"

Goofy Foot

could smolder them. It put a kinda good smell in the air, sort of sweet and deterred the "skeeters".

Gorge, the guy I met on the beach, my landlord for now, told me he had an outdoor restaurant next door. He said "he wanted to open it up, but lacked the money for goods". I looked at his restaurant, and was impressed. It was a great outdoor restaurant, and he said "he would sell beer, drinks, tortas (sandwiches) and even some burgers. I was going to stay for three weeks, and told him "I'll lend you the money if you can pay me back by the time I leave here". He agreed, and I bought him some stock. He did well right away when the tourists came out during the day. For a while, I was even serving for him, just for fun. Kinda "cool" an American waiting tables for Mexicans in Mexico.

His wife Angel helped out. She was a lawyer in Tepic, I was told. She looked Brazilian in her fine features. He only stayed about two weeks, then fled with Angel, back to Tepic. He had made some money, and paid me back in full. I was very happy I had met them and hugged each as they left. Just when things got a little stale, a guy drove in, in a VW Van. He surfed with me, a couple of days right off! I had surfed there almost every day. It was a good spot, right out front, which had a killer right wave. I had a board, so had everything I needed and Rob to surf with.

San Blas is a sleepy little town about ten miles from La Islita. It is the center of that area, with a square in the middle of town with a big open gazebo, and a big really old church at the one end. It was a great place to go in the evening, so I mostly did. There was usually an outdoor show, or band. There was always a lot of people, just romancing, playing with their kids; or kids playing with kids. I'd get a Fria Quamis en Papel (cold quart wrapped in newspaper), to drink while we hung there. Rob always transported us in his van. Besides enjoying a good time in the square, we could get my supplies also.

We talked to some people that said "they had been robbed on the way from La Islita". When they slowed down to cross a dry creek, a couple of Mexicans were standing near a hay cart, and had rifles stashed in the hay. They pulled them out and demanded all their pesos. Most travelers don't carry all their money at once, just for this reason. Fortunately this was the case for them. We decided to really watch out for those bandits. One night when we went in to San Blas, Rob met a cute little Mexican "Dish" at the square. He was all "hot and bothered" and claimed he was going to get some local tuna"! He continued to see this little "cutie".

When we got back we went out night surfing. The locals were yelling "jaws" and kinda grunting, but we just kept surfing. They were referring to sharks in the dark water. Rob was a diabetic, and had to shoot insulin every day. Once he said "You will have to get out of the van, because I have to shoot up now, and I might cry"! I can see how shooting up every day, sometimes multiple times, can wear on a guy. The only time I saw Rob after that, was in San Blas. I saw him go by a few times with his new love, and what looked like the whole family in his van. I guess he was paying after all for that "Local Tuna" by catering to her whole family.

Bob, a new resident, moved in across the cove from me. I heard he was a tough, wild man from the locals, who called him "el Loco", or something like that. I approached him with caution. He didn't seem too bad, and he had a plan. He noticed a local guy named Ernesto, had a small boat and a hundred meters of gillnet, sitting in his front yard. We made a deal with him so that we used his net and boat, and we were to give him most of the catch. We'd keep a few Sierras for entertaining people from town. We decided that people from town could provide the drink, and we would barbecue enough fish for all. The net was giving Bob and I about forty kilos of fish twice a day. I even had a good pot connection there called Azule (blue). With all the surfing I was really living it up. The catch started declining, because we couldn't patch all the shark holes fast enough. We were surfing out there at dark? Uhhh!

Bob took off for somewhere else down the "Gringo Trail", so I decided to split also. I went back to Punta de Mita, hoping to find Iquana was back. He wasn't back, so I put the board back under his palappa.

The guy the locals called "The Monkey Surfer" was there with his "squeeze". There wasn't any big waves, but he had a small, fast sailboat. We sailed around there a lot, and even caught Sierras out of the blue there with my "can line".

Finally the waves came up, and we started surfing again. I bought a nice medium sized pintail Gordon Smith board from the "Monkey Surfer". He really was the "Monkey Surfer" because of the way he jumped up and down, on the board. The surfing was a thrill there, except once a basking shark came right up and by us in the surf. He was about five meters, and I had to clean my shorts out when we got to shore!

Most everything had gone real well this trip, except I missed my old buddy Racooms. He never came up from that ill-fated scuba dive. I swam as fast as I could looking for bubbles in front of me, but couldn't find him anywhere near where I saw him last. I couldn't see the hand in front of my face the visibility was so bad, and I have never seen it anywhere near that bad since. I frantically crisscrossed the area looking for my buddy, but couldn't find him. There was a house near the water, so I kicked off my fins, and ran to the patio door. I yelled at the lady inside, telling her, "call 911", and tell them "lost diver at Agate Pass Bridge" and to put a rescue team in there! Then I went back down, put my fins on, and resumed my search. I kept searching until the Coast Guard came along and made me get out of the water. Exhausted when I stepped out of the water onto the beach, a whole slew of cameras, and reporters were in my face. I had just lost one of my best buddies and understandably just couldn't talk to anyone about the details.

A few months later the coroner called Gregamo and I over to identify a body. It was just a skeleton, but had a weight belt on, and both fins. Gregamo and I knew this was Racooms by the fins and belt. I believe he had an aneurysm, and was out of his mind, as he swam the wrong way, he was much too good a diver to leave his weight belt on. Anyway I looked at it; I had lost my good buddy, and felt like hell for quite a time after that.

I had trouble getting out of Mexico, because I didn't have the departure fees. I started selling some of my stuff at the airport to get it. Finally when my knife, and a blues harp were sold, I had the funds. I was to fly on an Alaska Airlines nonstop to Seattle.

A good buddy, and his wife, gave me a new sailboard as a bonus on a home improvement job. That would get me going on many sailboard / windsurfing adventures. I started sail boarding on my lake. There was good wind from the north May thru October. I struggled at first, but got good at reading wind and tacking. I could tack up to the north end of the lake; go through the swampy end with submerged logs sticking up. What a silent way to tour a pond.

I started going out to Silverville on the salt water. It lined up well for a south or southwest wind. The first time I went warp speed was here - what a rush. I really wasn't on a short board, but caught the wind just right, and skipped along for about two miles at warp speed.

There was starting to be talk about sailing at the Gorge and knew I had to try it.

CHAPTER 24

THE GORGE AT WARP SPEED

I got an old station wagon from my buddy Louis. We cut the top off behind the windshield with my reciprocating saw. Then I threw my old big board and a couple of sails etc. in my car and headed out to the Gorge.

A hitchhiker rode from Camas to Hood River with me and was good company, except he managed to "swipe" my "pot" without me knowing till later. I slept in the car that night with a tarp over me; got up in the morning, and put my log in the water. I was impressed with the wind in the area because it blew hard the whole time I was there. My board was big as a log, but I was determined to make it work for now.

I pushed off and stood on the board trying over and over to get my sail up, and finally got up and planing. A big gust came up, and I was hitting warp speed, and loving it. After a long run, I went down, and couldn't get the sail up, so couldn't go back the other way. I finally got to the bank, and pulled my log out of the water. I was hooked now, and just wanted to go "Warp speed" as much as possible.

The difference between sail boarding and windsurfing is as much as forty miles an hour. Sailboards are big and bulky, maybe 230 litres volume. Windsurfing boards are as small as sixty litres volume. On a log a sailor stands on the board and pulls the sail up. On a small board a sailor lays in the water and pushes the sail up until the wind catches the soil. It then pulls the sailor out of the water and up on the board. It is done this way because a small board won't hold a sailors weight and will just sink. When I'm finally standing on the small board I hook to my harness line that is part of the boom I'm holding in my hands I'm ready to hit "warp speed" because my feet are in the board straps and my body is leaning out holding all the weight and torque. What a "rush"!

I ended up getting a Sea Trend ATV at eighty four liters. I kept getting smaller and lighter weight gear - a lot of carbon fiber. That stuff is incredibly strong for its light weight.

If I could get help on my carving skills, I would be a lot better, and dryer. Carving is at the end of a run, when you want to turn and go back the other way, without getting wet. It involves stepping to the other side of the board while turning the sail. It was always a tossup whether I could get a good carve or not. I had good days when I could get a dozen in and bad days only making half of my carves, or less sometimes. Its heaven on earth when we can go fifty miles an hour, just a few inches off the water. When I see a good ramp in a wave, I jump it. I've been riding along at warp speed, and seen a guy upside down, about six meters high next to me. Most of the best windsurfers in the world have competed at the Gorge. It's not uncommon to be windsurfing next to one or more pros, and sometimes they'll show off. I never got that good, but usually was one of the fastest out there anyway.

The Gorge is a weather phenomenon, where the cold moist air of the ocean, seeks the hot dry air up in the desert of Eastern Washington. Since there are a lot of south, southwest winds, and the Gorge goes east then turns north about halfway along; the whole Gorge gets good wind, but it gets better as one goes east, and the wind even turns north with the Columbia

River. There's room for thousands of windsurfers because there are so many places to go out.

There's big waves at places like Swell City, Doug's Beach. Then there's places like Stevenson, Nuclear alley, and the Hood River Park entrance that have reasonably flat water. Then there's some places like Swell City, Roweena and Bingen that have both.

Most all the places charge for use of a place to put your gear together and go in the water. It's usually five to ten dollars, and for the fun we get, it's well worth it. Almost all have bathrooms. The girl that collected money at Swell City, had a good move, where she could throw her sail down, and it bounced right back up in her hands. Pretty impressive while she's still traveling at twenty five M.P.H.

I made many trips down, and intend to go as long as possible. I used to go to Swell City a lot, but lately I go to a place in Oregon called Roweena. I get out about nine in the morning, before most get it together and usually get at least an hour before anyone else shows. Sometimes I got someone to go out with me for safety's sake. It's easy to plane at warp speed most all day there. It's really filled in, which means no holes, where the wind is inconsistent. That's why I started getting away from Swell City. It was getting "holy" every time I went there, as of late. The river twists, and turns with high rock cliffs on each side that turn into hills and mountains. It's a beautiful place, as besides the river and its' beautiful landscape, there are Mount Adams in Washington but also Mount Hood in Oregon in view. It's a beautiful sight for sure.

In this kind of atmosphere, can you imagine going along at forty five MPH; just the fin in the water. I'm leaning back hard, butt just a few inches, as well as shoulders, from the water. When I'm that close to the water its' just "whipping' by. I see a ramp in a wave coming, and take it and jump. I take a little pressure off my legs, and stand up a little while I'm in the air, so I don't spin out on landing. Now I'm in flat water, where the wind is good and the water just has chop. Now I'm just ripping as fast as I can go. The windsurfing speed record is 74 MPH last I heard. Because of the twists and turns of the river, there are many different scenarios at the launch sites.

On a few occasions the wind just completely stopped, and I almost got stranded, trying to paddle my board and sail off the river. Sometimes the wind died so much, the wind couldn't get me out of the water. I had to stand on my board that would sink a foot or two under the water and at the same time pull my sail in, and barely be able to sail back in. If I could get going at all, the board would come up to the top of the water. Fortunately that hardly ever happened because it was slow and tiring, but a lot better than paddling in with all the drag of the sail.

Hood River in the early nineties was a hub of activity, because windsurfing was all the rage, and there were thousands of boarders. There were more windsurfing shops than any other kind of shops. Fashion shops, and hoidy - toidy restaurants followed, and the place was buzzing! The bars had good musicians, and other acts playing regularly.

I usually camped at tunnel 2 campground on the Washington side near Swell City. It was free but it was shut down because locals and fisherman "trashed" it. One night a guy came along, and said the owners wanted to "shut the place down because of the trashing". He said he knew the phone number of the owner and wanted to know if I would talk to the guy. I told him "yes". We got him to back off for now, but it wouldn't last. We noticed an old travel trailer wiped out at the end of the road, along with other crap. No wonder the owner got mad and eventually shut it down for good.

Besides being free it was "cool", because it was next to a lake called Drano. It was separated from the Columbia River by the road and railroad tracks. All hours big, long trains came by. My true love, and I were sleeping in the canopy of my pickup, the first time I stayed there with her. The train came along at about eleven pm. The tunnel is parallel to the camp ground and ends right in front of the campground. I opened my eyes to watch her in the moonlight. When the train came we could feel the ground shake a little, kind of a vibration in the air. I could see her eyes pop open, then suddenly there was a loud deafening roar, just a little ways away as the train cleared the tunnel. She sat right up startled, and almost put her head through the canopy. It was fun being down there with her. She dropped me, and my equipment, off at Swell City or the Hatchery, or maybe the Park, and went to Hood River shopping while I windsurfed. It was a free place but after Tunnel 2 campground was trashed and closed up I had to find different areas to camp. It isn't easy to find free camp areas in Washington and Oregon because the cops could run me out if not in a designated camp area. Most parks are for day use only, but I managed to find my overnight camp spots anyway.

I found a good spot on the side hill overlooking
Roweena. Good camping and my favorite spot to windsurf; how
could it get better than that?

Sail boarding is so good at my lake, I tried to make a
business out of it, by starting the Riviera Sailboard Club. It
wasn't zoned for business so the county managed to "shut me
down". I really wasn't getting many customers anyway and it
was cutting into my windsurfing time.

My next trip was to Oahu Hawaii. I met an old friend
Mitzi, and her boyfriend at Waikiki. She had grown up across
the point from me, and was a good friend of my younger brother.
Waikiki wasn't my type of place, but I had a good time surfing at
Ala Moana Park nearby. Also Mitzi, and her boyfriend were fun
to hang with in the evening. We watched Peewees Big
Adventure at her apartment one night - what a funny, goofy
movie! I flew to Lanai and met Maria there. We were just
getting along enough to have a good time. We stayed in a little
lagoon that had no one, except those that came over on day trips.
There were dolphins in the lagoon, and it was just gorgeous.
The next day we paid a tour boat to take us back to Maui. I
always thought Maui was the jewel of the Hawaiian Islands.
There's so much to do there, snorkeling, biking down the
volcano, touring, and the historical whaling is on display there.
We always stayed in Paia, and this time was no different. I knew
a guy there in Paia that rented out lots of houses, so could always
get one from him. We rented a car, and went down to the Pools
of the Seven Virgins. It is a series of seven pools that lead from
the ocean, and the trail along the pools eventually ends up at a
hundred meter waterfall. Each pool has cliffs around them, and

it is family tradition to swim across each pool and dive into each. Some of the cliffs are twenty meters high. I always dove instead of jumping, because I deemed it safer. I've seen most injuries from people jumping feet first, then falling over backwards, and sustaining back injuries.

Before we got to the big waterfall about two miles up, we came to a huge, very dark bamboo forest. Its' an all day long adventure there. I always thought we are so fortunate to live on the West Coast, and be so close to Hawaii. From what I've seen traveling all over the world, Hawaii is the most beautiful islands of them all!

Our next stop was on the big island, specifically the Kona Coast. We went up to Spencer Park on the top end of Kona one night. The snorkeling was good near there, but what really caught my attention was a big stone sacrificial altar sitting on the hill above the park. There is a big lawn that went between the altar and the park. We set up sleeping on this lawn, and after dark went up to the altar. It clearly read "taboo", so we thought we would be all right after dark. It was laid out in a round pattern, with stone rooms lining the hallway coming in. Then it opened up into the alter that sat in the center of the stone bleachers. It was open to the sea on one side, and had an incredible view of the island and ocean below. Five thousand years ago, the Hawaiians hauled all those, mostly black rocks from the ocean below to build this monument.

There was an ancient trail that ran along the side of the altar. It was of red earth, and was so hard my knife wouldn't even mark it. All those feet for five thousand years had really compacted it.

To make things even better, there was a full eclipse of the moon that night. It was magic laying on that lawn, watching it all. This was one of those nights that would stick in my mind forever.

The next day we went down to Captain Cook, a little town where he was killed by the natives. What a great man - he found most of the islands in the Pacific Ocean including the Hawaiian Islands!

We flew out to Kauai and were greeted by a large squall when we landed. It was raining buckets of water, but at least it was warm, and we made our way up to a cheap car rental place in the pouring rain. Us Washingtonians aren't too scared of the rain in fact they say we don't tan we rust. We rented an old car that was almost completely rusted out, and sounded like crap even wobbled down the road, but it got us around just fine. We took off for Hanalei Bay, as I knew there was good surfing there.

We needed a place to camp that night, and settled on a remote place near the water, where mostly locals hung. We were walking the beach when we came across a big turtle. She was like in a trance. We could see she was alive, because her egg shooter was moving when I rubbed her underside. About then a half dozen Hawaiians showed up, and hauled the turtle up to their camp. They probably cooked it up. We didn't like that much, but it is their island after all.

The following morning we drove to Hanalei Bay. There was good surfing in two spots. One spot had medium pushy waves, while another spot off the point had big mushy waves. I liked both spots.

I'd had a couple of good days surfing and had been in the islands quite a while, but had to go to Oahu, and back home. I got home and settled in to my concrete work. Gregamo was drinking too much, and wasn't always ready to work, so I got Mickey to work full time.

It was getting near winter, and I wanted to go to a warm spot. I heard of a place called Margarita - an island off Venezuela. Seems a guy from Portland had discovered it, and wrote an article in the Windsurfing Magazine I was reading. February was the peak month, and I was going there then. I took all my gear, including two boards in a big box.

When I landed at Caracas Airport, there was a riot going on outside, and people were locked out by cops, and were beating on the windows. Luckily I kept a lot of change on me, and paid a few guys to get me, and my stuff to the bus. I had to ride a bus down the coast a few hours, then take a ferry over to Margarita.

Turned out the guy from Portland that wrote the article was there, along with some others from the Gorge. We had a good time, and the wind was hard, and steady every day. I enjoyed it so much I sailed almost every day. I even sold my extra short board to a guy working there that was from Tigard Oregon, so didn't have to haul it back. On my one day off, I got a little Russian rental car, and toured the island. It was ugly, but I couldn't believe the prices there. Gas was twenty two cents a gallon; rum was less than two dollars a fifth; and I got a new Casio watch for under four dollars. They said things were cheap because it was an "Open Port", and there were no taxes. Sounded good to me. I had a great trip to Margarita, but was very tired, and beat up. It was open - ocean windsurfing there as long as I could get someone else to go. We could go a couple of miles out in the ocean at "warp speed" and it really beat me up because there were small to medium waves there.

I was beginning to gather up a few rentals back home, and bought another when I returned. We were making "beater houses" into good rentals, and it was really paying off. I had about six now. I was doing less, and less concrete work and remodeling more, which suited me just fine. I also built a new home on five acres I bought earlier. It turned out beautiful, and overlooked a fine seven meter waterfall, that was quiet in the summer, and noisy in the winter. It froze up once, and looked so beautiful that way.

It was the end of the road for Maria, and I. We enjoyed it while it lasted, and even lived with her at her house for a few months. I felt bad for her son, who I'm sure didn't understand our splitting up.

Because I sold the waterfall house, I lived at Maria's for a while and kept the six and a half acres I bought next to the five acres with the house.

We had once had a small rock festival on that property called the "Pig Eater Convention". We had day, and night bands playing on the stage we set up. We went thru sixty seven kegs of beer at that one. It was the follow up to the "Beef Eaters Convention" we had at a buddy's place, in which we went through seventy kegs of beer.

Mickey, and I played a couple of J. Giels songs, we had rehearsed, at this "Pig Eaters Convention". The crowd seemed to like "Wammer - Jammer" a lot. We kinda had an act we did between songs. We both had suits on with flour on our upper lip, to resemble cocaine. We had a baggy full of flour, and a teaspoon, and Mickey would turn his guitar, and hit the bag, and dump it. Then we'd both moan into the microphone. He also had a big hole cut in his suit pants so his butt was showing, and would turn to his amp with his ass showing and say "Bear with me". We went into our next song, "First I look in the Purse". It was fun! For months after that party, pot plants sprouted up from the "roaches" and seeds that had been dropped. They kinda grew like vines along the ground because I'd accidentally drove and ran over them.

My good buddy Gregamo died! That meant Gregamo and his only brother Racooms were both dead. His family gave me some sort of story about a heart defect, but I knew he had died the way Skip did - drowning on his own puke. The worst part about it was we were not on good terms when he died. He had pissed my couch when he stayed over one night earlier. I'll never forget when he got so smashed, he got up in the middle of the night, and shit on a chair, got back in bed, skid marks on the sheets and all. The next morning he got up, and blamed his dog for it. He lived by the drink, and he died by the drink.

Rob had come down from Canada to dive the San Juan's with me. I hadn't seen or heard from him, since I spent time with him, and his topless girlfriend at Punta De Mita. He had dumped her, but it was a real pleasure to dive with him in the Juans.

We speared lots of fish on our dives. We cut them up and put the meat in a bucket of water to trade for beer, wine, or whatever on the docks of Roach Harbor. We did well, and it was a good way to meet, and talk to people. At last Rob had to return to Canada and I took my boat back home.

When I returned home I went over to my dive buddy Rick's house to tell him all about my diving in the Juans. There is no coral there, but there are big rocks, big kelp beds, and lots of big beautiful Sea Anemones of all colors. We had seen ling cod, we guessed would go twenty kilos. There are also Scallops, Abalone, and Swimmer Scallops. Swimmer Scallops start swimming off when they sense someone near. They resemble false teeth swimming off, and we grabbed them, and put them in my bag, like grabbing them right out of the air.

When I walked into Rick's, Super Tramp's Crime of the Century was playing - what a great album! After that was over we put Styx's Miss America on, also a great album. We liked their music a lot, but when I saw them at the Gorge Amphitheatre, they sounded real tight, but seemed very vain. By now Frog was living in a trailer on a six and a half acre place I owned. He was a young, happy guy, who enjoyed living on property right next to where he grew up. My daughter turned out to be such a great "kid". I really enjoyed having her around.

I was hanging with a girl I'd known for a long time named Karry. We had finally got together, and I was really enjoying my time with her. She had a daughter that was nineteen or so, and seemed to hate my guts - I was glad she had her own place, so I didn't have to see her much!

Karry and I set out to see The Moody Blues at the Paramount in Seattle. The Paramount is an old turn of the century theatre that was remodeled and looks great inside, with

huge chandeliers, lots of balconies, and a dome ceiling. We
snuck in a bottle of wine, and sat in a couple of seats right down
front. The Moody Blues sounded great, and it wasn't long
before we were in the aisle dancing, along with some of the other
more rowdy types. It turned out to be a great concert, and Karry
seemed to really enjoy it. It was "high energy" and we were real
tired when it was over.

　　　　When we got down to the ferry, we didn't have enough
money left to get us on the boat. I spotted a truck, and camper in
line to go on the boat. No one was in it right then, so Karry and I
got in the back, and covered ourselves up in the bed. The people
came back, and drove on the boat unaware of us in back. When
we stopped on the boat, they got out, and left the car deck. We
peeked out of the window as they were walking away. We went
upstairs, and when I saw the driver sitting, we walked over and
shook his hand and said "thanks for the ride". Of course he had
no idea what I was talking about, and left him wondering. We
had some other adventures sneaking on the boat. Once Racooms
and I didn't have enough to get all three of us on the boat, so
Nap drove while we got in the trunk. We lit up a joint in the
trunk, and as we drove on, the trunk popped open from the bump
entering the car deck. A big cloud of smoke rolled out, as well
as our heads popped up. One of the crew started yelling at us,
and fortunately Nap took off, and we parked and got out, and
went right upstairs before they could catch up to us. On another
occasion Jimmy and a girl got in the trunk. We got up to the
booth to pay. They started getting it on back there, and the car
was bouncing slightly up and down. Fortunately the teller didn't
say anything, but I'm sure he noticed because he had a pretty
good grin going as we left.

I heard a friend of mine called "Poodle head", because of his big, blond "fro", got in a wreck on the freeway near Tacoma. A guy was up front driving while "Poodle Head" and a girl were getting it on in the back seat. The driver swerved, and rolled the car. "Poodle Head" and the girl were both ejected - naked!

Nap, and Racooms were coming back out of money. They went down to the ferry, and pondered the situation. They decided to lay flat on the top of a tractor -trailer. They climbed up a ladder on the back of the trailer, and laid down. What they didn't know was there was a ferry office right up above, where they could see everything going on. They saw them both up there, so they sent a guy down to bang on the side of the trailer, and say "you two come on down"! They finally came down, and Nap had worn a white suit, and it was dirty, and "wiped out". They still didn't have a way across the water because they were denied access to the ferry!

J.J., Susie, Jimmy, Lola, Julie, and I all went together to an outdoor concert in the stadium at Seattle Center. There were a few good sounding bands including Bob Seeger. I liked all of them, especially Heart, but Bob Seeger wasn't together. I saw him a couple of years later, and he was great. His songs had changed a lot for the better. We snuck in about four bottles of "Mad Dog". It did the trick, and we stuck the last one in the bushes on the way out, and I'll be dammed if it wasn't there two weeks later when we went to another concert. I spotted it gleaming in the bushes.

CHAPTER 25

GREAT BARRIER REEF

I was getting real itchy to go on a big trip. I decided to go to Queensland Australia for three weeks.

After I had taken care of business, I left on a Quantas flight for Cairns. That was the closest spot to embark to the Great Barrier Reef.

I did my usual packing, lots of shorts, a few kinds of shirts, all shapes but I always pack a long sleeve white shirt. When I get to a hot place, being tall, and fair, I get burned easy, even though I go to a tanning salon at least six times, before leaving. So for the first week I wear that shirt from ten a.m. to five p.m. to protect me during the hottest part of the day.

I take my own personal shoes, called karachees. I take converse style, black and white tennis shoes, and cut out sections of black everywhere. The result is a distinctive shoe that can be worn in, or out of the water. Because I hang my hammock between two trees or palms, I take a full size sheet and can wrap up like a taco if the bugs are bad. I also take a Mexican blanket with a neck hole cut in it, in case it gets cool. If I go down from drink I'm ready to pass out in it. A medicine kit with band aids, Green Mountain Skidders Medicine (Diahrea), Amosan, aspirin, charcoal pills, baby oil, ace bandage, Sudaphed, ear drops, New Skin, Neosporin, and Carmex is a must. These things will take care of most problems. I take a mess kit with, oil, garlic, salt, and pepper; maybe some rice, and Top Ramen. I like to be ready to camp, if I don't find other accommodations.

Cairns (pronounced Cans) is a medium size town, close to the sea. I didn't like the beach much. It was on a river. Since I'm a "water guy", I really was looking for better places, and headed out on a bus for Port Douglas. Port Douglas is really the best access to the Great Barrier Reef. There was a pretty good Hostel there so I stayed for a night. The beach wasn't so good there, as it was only slightly clearer than the water on Cairns beach. We had to swim inside a "Jellyfish Net". It is used to protect swimmers from the deadly Box Jellyfish! I walked down the local dock the next morning just to look for something good. As I walked by about a sixty five footer, a guy on board asked me "Do you want to go out to the Great Barrier diving for half price". Half price was seven hundred fifty dollars for 10 days diving - all included. I said "sure", and he informed me I had to have my "stuff" aboard in a half hour. I went back to the hostel, and got my stuff, including my dive gear. Soon I was heading out to the Great Barrier outer reef in the Coral Sea. There were three American ladies on board, two just a little younger than me, and one of the sister's eighteen year old daughter. Then there was a German guy Walter we liked a lot, a great Aussie guy, an old couple, a young German girl named Marin, and an Austrian party of five adults.

The crew consisted of Soji our Japanese dive master; the captain Jack, and two brothers Simon and Nigel. Simon, and Nigel were the owner's sons. Nigel was pretty subdued, but Simon was a real character, well known around Port Douglas. They right away took my Hawaiian sling lance away and stashed it below decks. There would be no fish shooting on the Great

Barrier because it was unlawful. They informed me we could fish with a hand line off the boat at night, at anchor. Soji also fished at night, and had brought bait along. Our first dive was the usual check out dive, designed to see how well we could dive. I wouldn't have any problems, having done about eight hundred dives, most in the Puget Sound. This dive was near Lizard Island in the near side of the reef. The water wasn't so clean, and the sea life not so abundant. I buddied - up with Diane, the American woman without a daughter. She was a relatively new diver, so I set about going it easy, and building her confidence. She turned out to be a good dive - buddy. We got on with this dive, and moved out to the outer reef beyond. I fished that evening, off the back of the boat with Soji. That was the last evening anyone fished with me, until later in the trip when Walter joined me. I caught a lot of fish; some of them big, but had to throw them all back because they were toxic, as they were feeding on small fish, that were poisoned by eating coral.

The next day we saw a sight I'll never forget. Diane and I were diving a balmy. A balmy is a round coral mass in the open under water. Sometimes there are multiple balmies in an area. This was the case here. We came around the far side of the balmy, and there was a big Cuddle Fish near the edge. It was flashing many colors on the main part of its body with a ring of flashing colors, running around its body fringe. As we watched, it put one of its arms out, and grabbed a small fish off the balmy. That was why it was pulsating such colors, because it was excited by the hunt. At any rate it was an incredible sight. On our next dive the dive master fed some big Potato Cod in front of us. They were all about sixty to ninety kilos. I was glad

I wasn't the one feeding them pilchards by hand. Groupers were knifing in and taking Soji's bait, and one cut his hand open pretty badly.

The third dive that day took place where we could see two or three meter sharks laying all over the bottom. When we got down there it was kind of spooky, diving around all those Mako Sharks. It was Diane's first experience with sharks, and I had to lead her by the hand most of that dive. We were last back to the boat as usual. We really enjoyed our dives, and didn't want them to end. We told Simon to make sure we were back to the boat before they moved. A couple had been left out at sea, diving out of Port Douglas recently. They made a movie out of it later.

That afternoon I finally caught a fish we could eat, in the form of a big Sea Trout. Our cook cooked it that night for dinner, and it was delish.

That night I slept on the deck, because I can't stand air conditioning, or sleeping below deck in the sleeping quarters. It was very comfortable with the cool sea breeze and all, until one night when I got too close to the edge, and rolled off into the water. What a rude awakening that was, waking up blubbering in the ocean.

The next day we went to an underwater cave. When we got to the entrance, Soji put a finger to his lips to give us the sign to be quiet. We could see why because there was a four meter Hammerhead shark laying on the bottom with a few smaller Makos. We swam quietly over the top of these sharks. This shark was so big, my heart was pounding, but we managed to get out of the cave without spooking them.

That night we went on a night dive, and witnessed the coral releasing its eggs. It rarely happens, only on a full moon. I felt privileged to witness it. There were many fish, and other critters feeding on the coral eggs that were being released in a cloud.

I enjoyed playing tricks on Simon. He was leaning over the rail - butt crack showing. I came along, and dumped a bowl of ice down his shorts. As usual he declared "your ass is grass". The Aussie guy and I were always arguing, who trashed the English language worse - Americans or Aussies. The Aussies change a lot of A's to I's when they speak; and I asked him "if cookies are called biqies, then what are bisquits called"? It was all good natured fun.

Skipper Jack was a good guitar player, as was Marin, so sometimes I got my harp out, and we jammed together. They were both much better musicians than I, but it was fun anyway. The water out there was very clear, and the fish really shown. We got to know the names of some of the more common fish, such as Parrots, Fusiliers, File, Damsels, etc. Everything about this trip was outstanding, the divers, the boat, the crew, even the good meals cooked up by Nigel's wife. One night we traveled all night, and it was so rough, we could feel the boat sliding down waves. We were heading out into the Coral Sea, and that night I had to sleep below decks. The trip was worth it. The sea was even clearer, the coral even more pristine, and it turned very calm.

Come on in the water is fine.

Most days a customs plane flew over, and checked us out. Seems the Aussies are really protective of the reef, because some Indonesians were raping the reef. I guess when customs catches them they tow the boat in to shore; burn it, and throw the crew in jail. They don't "mess around"!

Our next dive had Giant Clams that were a meter or more across. Simon told me the poachers put a stick between the shells, so the clams couldn't close, then cut out the inside. Some of these clams were said to be two hundred fifty years old. I don't guess they could recover easily if they were to be over harvested.

We noticed when the cook threw the food scraps out, a cloud of Perch would feed on it, so I started putting a little piece of bacon on my hook, and line, and throwing it in with the scraps. I was getting about a half dozen Perch each time. Everyone on the boat appreciated the fresh fish. We finished up our diving, and had a party on one of the low islands on the way back. We drank a lot, bar-b-qued, and did a lot of singing, and playing instruments. I noticed at the end of the night, Simon and Marin ended up going off together. The next day, on the last leg back to port, we were pondering what to do next. Diane said "she and the other two were going to get a rental car, and head north into Queensland". She wanted to know if I wanted to come along. It sounded good, and after we reached port, we set out. I had been a real gentleman to these three, and they felt real comfortable with me. The one was too young, and the Mom and Aunt weren't real beauties, in fact they were "amazons", but they were fun to be with.

When we got to the Daintree River, we found we couldn't take the rental car any further, so we left it, and after a short ferry ride, we hitch-hiked on the other side. The guy we rode with told me an American couple, wanted a picture of his wife standing in the Daintree River, so she stepped out to waist deep water and posed. A big Croc took her, and he had to pay for a search to try to find her. By dragging they found her, because the Croc had placed her under the water to soften her up so it could eat her later. As if it wasn't bad enough that he lost his wife, then he had to pay for the search. Served him right since there are signs declaring "Crocs - do not swim" all over the river. Subsequently the Aussies have a saying "if you want to find a croc throw in a yank"!

Out hiking one day we saw a guy that had a couple of Fruit Bats hanging on him. He was an advocate of protecting them. He wasn't at all popular with farmers, because Fruit Bats take only a bite or two out of fruit, then move on to the next. Farmers lose a lot of fruit to them. I happened to have a Batman hat on and gave it to him. He looked better than I wearing it, since he also had that Fruit Bat hanging on his shirt.

We stayed in a jungle hut, and found a croc free stream nearby that served as a swimming hole. On the way back, we stayed in a little trailer at a guy's place, and had some good partying one night with him and his wife. We also met another Aussie there that traveled with us for a few days. We discovered that when I flushed the toilet, the water really does swirl the opposite way there. It swirls counter clockwise below the equator evidently.

Clam Chowder for two hundred.

"You First – No you first"

One evening as the five of us were walking in the moonlight, up on the plateau, I almost stepped on a big Tiger Snake. He laid across the dirt road motionless. They are poisonous, and it could have been bad for me. Between the crocs, centipedes, snakes, spiders; and so on, there are a lot of things to get someone "Down Under"!

We finally went back to our rental car, because the girls had to fly out. I still had a week or so left. The girls dropped me off at the dock at Port Douglas. I remembered Nigel telling me they were going back out on a different part of the reef for a few days. Marin was the only person I knew on this trip, and "buddied up" with her for our diving. Most of the guests were really old, and pretty sedentary. There was a young American couple that I didn't get along with very well. Simon was not along, but Nigel was. His Dad who owned the boat was along on this trip also.

On one dive I was partnered with their Dad, because Marin couldn't go. We found a fishing line laying on the bottom that led to about a meter hole in the reef. Their Dad, William, started following this line until he got right in front of the hole. He gave the line a tug, a shark came flying out, and knocked his mask off. I thought I would drown laughing while watching all this. Earlier we were fishing off the boat when I caught a six foot Mako. I had to wrap the line around the cleat, and break him off - hence the line laying on the bottom with a shark on the end of it.

I kinda got in a little problem on the boat because William told me I could harvest some scallops. I did since he owned the boat, and thought he would know. He didn't, and they weren't happy with me or him.

The next day Marin, and I were diving together again. We got into the middle of about twenty Cuddle Fish, and it was impressive. Sometimes they look unimpressive until they get excited, then they put on a "color show". That was the case here, but they really put on a great show, and I haven't to this day seen that many together again. We also found a small octopus attached to a rock, and I told Marin I could show her a big octopus if she came to visit me at home. Puget Sound has the biggest octopus in the world; some fifty or sixty kilos and over six or more meters across.

After we got our diving out of the way, we had a party on one of the low Islands again. This trip was good, but not as good as the first time out.

When we got back to Port Douglas, Simon was there, and offered me a ride to Cairns. I said "Goodbye" to everyone and set out with Simon.

Upon arriving in Cairns I decided to catch a bus, and head south to try and find some surfing, windsurfing or both. The bus ride was uneventful, except I noticed lots of dead Kangaroos next to the road that had been hit. Reminded me of the deer back home lying next to the road.

I finally ended up in Noosa Head. There was windsurfing there, but it was in the mouth of a river and was marginal at best. I spent a half day at it mostly because the rental guy had pretty "crappy" gear and it wasn't as fun as with my good gear back home.

I stayed at a hostel for a couple of days, and was happy to be able to cook my own food. Prepared food in Australia is terrible tasting, much like English food.

I was due to fly out of Cairns back to America soon. I got on the bus and headed north because I found out the nearest surfing was way south and was running out of time. I went past Cairns a ways because I heard there was a great zoo to visit nearby. The place had a big croc that measured seven meters long. A guy led him out for public viewing. I could hardly believe how huge the croc was. What I didn't know at the time, was the guy who led him out was a young Steve Irwin. He didn't get famous until a year or two later. Upon seeing him when he became famous I knew I'd seen him. I could also tell by the way he talked. Even Aussies don't talk like he does.
I made my way back to Cairns and had a few hours to blow, so I looked around. One thing that struck me was the lack of wanted posters in the Post Office - there was only one! When I went to Brisbane, I also noticed the lack of police compared to Seattle. Australia just doesn't seem to have as much crime as we do in the U.S. which seemed odd because it was a former penal colony. They're present immigration laws will probably change that however.

On my long flight back home, I pondered trying to get together with my daughters Mom again, and get a real family going. Those thoughts were dashed when I returned. We went to a party at her house, and really thought we just wouldn't work. She was just so independent, and there just wasn't anything there anymore between us. We both truly loved our daughter, who brought us so much joy though.

I went back to work remodeling and concrete pouring, and contemplated my next trip. I decided on the Cayman Islands.

One great thing that happened was a call from Marin. She was in Seattle, and wanted to come visit me. I thought Karry might get a little jealous, but Marin was not a pretty girl, and Karry didn't mind her staying with me a couple of days. I told her in Australia I would show her a big octopus, and set about to do just that! I took her to the local dive shop, and fitted her with a full thick wetsuit, tank, and weight, as she had everything else. We went to the canal, and went down to about ten meters to a place where I had harvested a couple of big ones in my earlier days. Sure enough, I found one in a slit in the rock bottom. Now I don't harvest them, just get them to come out and play with them. I got this one to come out by being real patient, and showing it I could be trusted. It was about twenty kilos, and three meters across. I got it to spread out like a star, and even rub against me like a puppy dog. Marin's eyes were wide open in amazement. I kept trying to put her hand on it, but she wouldn't touch it. I was able to show her a big octopus in a big way! After her, and I partied with my friends and showed her the sights for a couple of days, she said her "goodbyes" and left. All she could talk about was our encounter with the big octopus and I had kept my promise. She was also, as was I, impressed with a Seattle D.J called "Raven". He played the best music there is. A few years earlier "Raven" and another D.J called "East" were doing skits on radio. The best one was their version of "Leave it to Beaver". It was so funny. Raven was still on the radio every day and I really enjoyed his music.

CHAPTER 26

CAYMANS

I got ready and took off to the Cayman Islands. I didn't take any scuba gear this time, just snorkeling gear, and everything I needed to be self-sufficient. It would be a good move, because I returned on a later trip equipped to scuba dive. On this trip I laid the ground work.

I ended up taking a flight to Houston; then to Miami; then to Grand Cayman from there. Grand Cayman is the largest, most popular, island of the three, which also includes Cayman Broc, and Little Cayman.

I went to a place called "Hell", and it looks like hell. It is a swamp with a field of weird looking, jagged rocks. There's a little post office there, and I sent out "Hell" post marked cards to some of my friends. Kind of a novelty I suppose. Next I went to Stingray Bay on the back side of the island. About ten of us went out on an open pontoon charter boat. We went out in this bay which was very turquoise in color, with a sandy bottom, and just stopped. About the time we started wondering why we were just sitting there, we noticed big black spots in the water coming at us from all directions. It was big stingrays, and soon we got in the water with them. The guide gave us bait, and told us to "keep our palms wide open with the bait in our palms". Soon we had a stingray feeding frenzy going. He said they "weren't dangerous", and they didn't seem to be as long as we followed his feeding instructions.

After that we went out to the only real reef in that bay,

Steve Irwin's Worst Nightmare

on the outskirts, and snorkeled for an hour. The real draw in this snorkeling spot, was a long line of pretty blue Fusiliers that never seemed to end.

We went back to the beach where we had embarked on this adventure. It was a beautiful beach, which had plenty of Coco Palms with the beautiful turquoise water in the background.

I heard there was some windsurfing going on at the end of the island, on the other side, called Tortuga, which means turtle. I got a rental scooter, and set out for Tortuga. I smoked a little with a local black guy in a place called Boddenville on the way out. I wouldn't travel with any pot, so smoked with him on the beach, and then gave him some cash for it. I was impressed with the guy because he didn't have attitude like some of the blacks back home.

When I got out to Tortuga, a hotel complex on the beach; sure enough a guy named Bruno had a windsurfing business set up, in a good little cove. I didn't waste any time in the water before going "warp speed" in the cove. I didn't get off on a good footing with Bruno. The boom I rented from him broke. Corrosion had gotten to it. Unlike the freshwater Gorge, the saltwater eats everything up. Like they say" corrosion is your enemy, and rust never sleeps"! I did go out for a few days here before moving on.

I wasn't going to sleep in any "stinking hotel", so found a place to hang my hammock on the beach in the Caribbean Grape. I was glad I had my hammock, since hermit crabs came out by the thousands at night, and the ground below me looked like it was moving! After a few days I went back toward town.

It's a tough job, but someone's got to do it.

I got kinda sick, and could only manage to hang in my hammock in the park for a couple of days. I had gone to a local "quack" and he said I just had "Tropical Fever", and gave me some pills to take.

There was a ship wreck out about a half mile in the bay, in about twenty meters of water. I got well again, and went for it. I put my snorkeling gear on, and swam all the way out there. Since twenty five meters was my max snorkeling depth, I could snorkel the wreck. There were already scuba diving boats out there, so this was a perfect opportunity to harass scuba divers. Sometimes while viewing the wreck, I could come up behind divers, and pull on their hoses to harass them. They would be surprised to see a snorkeler down there. After a half hour or so of good fun, I headed back. I was yelled at a couple of times by water skiers, but didn't pay much attention to them. I splashed and so on to get their attention, so I wouldn't get run over. I was really tired by the time I got back, and had no problem collapsing in my hammock, for a night's sleep. The next day I concluded I had pretty well done Grand Cayman, and wanted to get to Cayman Brac. Brac is far enough to take a jet to get there. When I arrived there I could see why they called it "Brac". It had a few bodies of brackish water on it like salt water swamps.

I was hitch-hiking on the island, pack on back, going nowhere in particular, when an older lady pulled up, and said "Get in". She said she was "Joyce" and we got along instantly. She said "she lived there part of the year, and that her husband hadn't joined her yet". I didn't get the idea she was trying to "hit on me" at all. She took me to the local bar where she seemed to know everyone. She just liked to be seen with younger guys.

She offered me a place to stay with her, and I accepted. She turned out to be a good friend. I learned a lot about the island from her. Brac had an extensive pirate history. The next day I set out for a place she said was "great snorkeling". Boy, was she right! I had to walk for an hour; then swim from rock to rock with my stuff on my head. The visibility was the best I had ever seen anywhere. It was about seventy five meters. There were nurse sharks everywhere, which are harmless, and a lot of pretty fish, and lobsters. At the end of my snorkel a big lobster came along, like it owned the place. I couldn't resist, and took it. When I got back that night Joyce and I cooked it up, and gorged ourselves - what a feast.

I noticed in the Caribbean there was always a big barracuda following me around. Once I took my can fishing line with a piece of chicken on the hook, out snorkeling with me. My plan was to catch a fish while snorkeling, and bring it in while in the water, but couldn't quite get a barracuda to take my bait. I always wanted to do different things, and that would have definitely been unique!

Joyce told me about a one day trip I could take to Little Cayman with a man named Frank Bodden. That last name seemed to be on about half the stuff in the islands. Anyway the next morning I went down to the local docks, and looked for Frank. He was there and along with seven others booked the excursion. He was a small guy, with glasses, and had a huge native wife.

Our first stop on Little Cayman was a place called Point of Sand. It was a pretty little lagoon that was loaded with lobsters. Frank was fond of rum, and we started drinking some. He had an old truck stashed on shore, and we went touring the

All I need is the Steak.

island while we drank rum. We went to a family's dive
compound, and met the whole family. They were very nice
native people, and had an all-inclusive dive operation going.
I would return at a later time to dive with them.

When we returned to the docks at Brac, Frank's big wife
was waiting, and wasn't very happy with his rum drinking. I
thought it was all pretty funny, and left happy with my day
thanks to Frank. I had the feeling these confrontations with his
wife over rum drinking had occurred before.

I went back to Joyce's, and found she had left for her
home in Dallas, but left instructions I could stay as long as I
wanted. I only stayed one night, and left the next day to Grand
Cayman.

When I returned to Grand, I was to leave a couple days
later, so got another scooter, and headed out past Tortuga to do
some snorkeling, and maybe some windsurfing on the way back.
I went to a place where there was calm water inside a small
barrier reef. There was a small opening in the reef, undoubtedly
where boats went in and out. I got sucked out of this opening
into the open sea. I thought I'd snorkel out there as long as I was
there. It was beautiful, and one of the first things I saw was a
huge spotted Eagle Ray gliding right by me. When they swim
they resemble a big bird flying - absolutely beautiful! There was
no way to get through the opening in the reef to get back to land,
because the current was too strong. I carefully went over the
shallow reef to get back, only receiving a couple small scrapes.
When I got back to Tortuga, there was no wind, so windsurfing
was out of the question, and moved on back to town. I flew out
that night on an uneventful flight back the way I came.

CHAPTER 27

THE LOVE OF MY LIFE

When I returned back home, I was invited to a get
together at my younger brothers. His wife, and three boys were
there, and I took my son and daughter. We had a great time
partying, and playing horse shoes. What really made the day
was the woman I met. Deener would be the love of my life. I
didn't know what to think at first, what with her big round
glasses that seemed to be all the rage right then. She was bubbly,
and outgoing though, and that caught my attention. She needed
an addition built onto her little house, and I decided to do it. At
that point when I started, I met her three boys, all just over ten
years old. I really didn't quite know what to think of them at
first. They seemed to be good boys, but didn't see them a lot.
They were usually at school, and when they came home they
usually plopped down in front of the television to play video
games. A guy came over a lot, and spent time with the boys, but
I gathered right away, he was not the father. Turned out he was
just a good friend, who really cared about the three boys and
their mom! I finally finished the job, but during the job I
couldn't help but notice she was pretty "hubba - hubba", and got
pretty close. She still owed me money after I was done, so on
one of my trips to try to collect from her, I asked her out.
We went out to a sorta high class seafood place. Then we just
hung together, and listened to tunes the rest of the evening at her
house. We dated for a while; then I kinda started hanging with
an old flame again. It wasn't long before I got back with Deener

again, and we dated for about another year or so. I finally
realized I loved this woman, and her boys, and asked her to
marry me. Her boys were best friends with my younger
brother's boys. They were almost as happy as I when her and
her boys said "yes"!

We decided to move in together right away but we both
had small houses. Her house was on two and half acres across
from Wildman Lake. The county gave us permission to build
another house on the property. We built a large new house up on
the hill, after our wedding. It all went well. We really came
together as a family, because we built our new house together.
Kind of a "Brady Bunch" experience. Fawn was thrilled to have
three new brothers about her age. The boys were happy to have
a new large home. They lived in a travel trailer next to our little
house, while Deener, Fawn and myself lived in the cabin until
we finished our new home on the hill. We got the kids to finish
their own rooms in the new house. My step dad had married my
mom, when she had three boys also, so it seemed natural –kinda
like deja vu.

I loved those boys, and we spent a lot of time camping,
and going out in my boat together. Once I put a stop to the video
games after school, the boys got pretty adventurous. The kids
were always running the neighborhood, and fishing in the lake.
Of course Fawn was getting to the age where she wasn't paying
any attention to me, and not much attention to any other family
members either. I was very concerned about her but a good
friend, who had gone through it too said "She'll come back
later".

We got a call from a friend about an acquaintance that
needed birds driven out of his attic. I went over, and met Ned,

and his wife. The screens in his bird blocks had failed, and the starlings had moved in. I got my ladder, replacement screen, and some bee spray, that sprayed about six or seven meters. It solved the problem, and Ned wanted to know if I could set a buoy for him, in the salt water out front of his house. He got the whole thing ready, and I returned with my scuba gear, ready to go. When I got finished setting the buoy, I still had half a tank of air left. One of my brothers, Jan had owned the house next door earlier, and I knew the turf underwater there pretty well, from previous dives. There was a huge rock in about fifteen meters of water nearby, and I headed that way. Ned was above me in a row boat when I reached the rock. There was a twenty kilo octopus hanging onto the rock. I worked it loose and went to the top with it. I started shoving it in Ned's row boat, and when Ned started pulling it into his boat, I told him "I am kidding, we don't want to keep him", and it went back down to the bottom. Ned said "you mean there's stuff like that down there"? "Yes there is and more"! Ned got certified to dive right away - he was hooked!

MAUI AGAIN

I made another trip to Maui, and of course it was great. Good windsurfing at Sprecklesville, Kehai, and the Airport. I also did some scuba diving at a little horseshoe shaped island called Molikini. The whole dive I could hear whales squealing. I'd never heard that before. There were a lot of Frog Fish, and turtles in the water. Frog fish stand on their fins and resemble a frog on the bottom.

I was able to go way out into the ocean at Kehai, after talking another windsurfer into going out there with me. It could be a disaster if I'm alone, and have an equipment break down all the way out there. There were whales and turtles surfacing everywhere.

I was camping out of my rental car out near Hana, when I awoke to a very windy, rainy morning. I took off back to Paia to "cop" some breakfast at a local pub - eatery called "Charlies". The entire island was without power, because of the storm. It was serious, because this was Super Bowl Sunday, and the Bills were playing the Cowboys. A guy pulled up in front with a big flatbed with an equally big generator on it. He proceeded to hook the big screen up, and we were able to watch the game. It was a thriller. The Bills missed a game winning field goal at the end of game, and the Cowboys prevailed. We were probably one of the few on the island that was able to see this great game! The next day I flew out, and again felt fortunate to live on the west coast, and be so close to these great islands.

When I got home, after hugging my whole new family - I got to work. I heard about a house in a fairly good hood that was for sale - cheap. When I went to look at it, I could hardly believe how rough it was, but it definitely had potential. About one quarter of the house was eaten, and infested by carpenter ants. The yard was completely filled with junk. Appliances, tires, garbage, etc. filled the yard. I got it so cheap, and was able to get a loan on it from a friend at the bank.

I recruited my oldest son Frog to help me on the project. We worked six months straight, but were able to make a great rental out of it. This house ended up becoming a gold mine I own to this day. I repaid my son for the work by giving him the three and a half acre parcel he was living on.

After this long haul, I was ready for some adventure. I had been diving locally with Ned, and we decided to do a dive trip together. We wanted to go to the Cayman Islands. I hadn't done any scuba diving when I was there the first time and I really wanted to. I knew we could do some world class diving on Little Cayman with the McCoy family. Ned had a friend Scotty that wanted to join us. After setting it up with the McCoys, we were ready to enjoy this great adventure.

Three Hour Lunch

CHAPTER 28

BLOODY BAY AND BEYOND

We left Sea-tac and flew straight away to Miami; then to Grand Cayman. We flew right out of Grand Cayman to Cayman Brac. My plan was to try to get to that beautiful Point of Sand by boat. I couldn't find Frank to once again take me and my buds to Point of Sand. We finally found a boat to take us to our sweet spot for a small fee. When we reached the point, it was all beautiful as I remembered it. We decided to camp there that night, and have McCoys pick us up in the morning. That evening after dark we went snorkeling with our lights, gloves and a bag. I knew from my previous visit there were a lot of lobsters there, and we were out to get some. We were snorkeling, side by side in about three meters of water when we came on a scene I'll never forget. A large lobster came out of a hole under a big rock. An octopus that was on top of the rock, jumped on top of the lobster and they began to wrestle right there. After a while the lobster got loose, and jetted off. It was like they put on a show just for us! Of course we ate lobster cooked in foil over our fire for late dinner. We got them to back into our hands, and they constrict when caught, which hurts without gloves.

That was a great experience, but we paid dearly. We were eaten alive by mosquitoes that night. My only defense was to wrap up like a taco in a king sized sheet. The next morning all three of us were all lumped up because the sheet wasn't real effective at keeping them off of us.

Just as planned we were picked up by McCoys. They are a good native family that run a dive operation. We got our accommodations in their compound, and set out to look at the little island better. It was just as my previous visit - very laid back. We also met our dive master, a little Scottish girl named Annie. She was fun to be around, and had this great high pitched giggle, that seemed to be in harmony with Ned's boisterous laugh. Anyone could easily hear them laughing in a crowd. The next day we went to the world famous Bloody Bay, where Black Bart had some pirate battles with the English. Scotty, Ned, Annie, one of the McCoy sons, and I went diving together. The Corals in this bay were great as well as pirate cannons, cannon balls etc. we saw laying on the bottom. There was an abundance of Groupers and lots of Corals that resembled big volcanoes, and huge sea fans.

After three good dives we returned to our compound, and had dinner. We were treated to Conk soup, made by Mrs. McCoy. Conk is a big crawling clam that is good, though I don't think it's as good as our Northwest clams.

The next day we did some shore dives; one of which was called "The School Bus". There's an old abandoned bus where we put in. This dive had the biggest old cannon we had ever seen. It had shot balls the size of my head. There were lots of lobster, and big schools of Barracuda, as well as Parrot, Hog, Snappers and Sea Snakes of all colors.

The next day only Ned, our dive master Annie, and I went diving. It was very rough on the water, and we were the only boat out. Annie was great, and would go anywhere we wanted her to take us. We dove three more times in Bloody Bay that day. Some of these dives had big schools of Glass fish.

They all move the same way at precisely the same time, and are mesmerizing to watch. They resemble a moving cloud. There were also Crocodile fish that really looked just like a crocodile laying on the bottom. The next day was just as rough, and only Ned, Annie, and I went out again. We dove a different set of dives away from Bloody Bay. These weren't quite as good, but were still very good. These dives had a lot of Giant Sea Fans. I'd seen Sea Fans before, but there were more here, and they were bigger, and more colorful. I watched a big Grouper attack and eat a smaller fish, while another tried to push his way in. One of these dives was a steep wall dive that had multiple Eagle Rays cruising the wall. Annie was a fairly new dive master, and hadn't seen a lot of the things we were seeing before, and was also very excited. Sometimes the best part of diving is when we come up to shallow water, near the end of the dive. I like to stay in one place, and watch the reef, as it is a community of fish, with different situations going on. Fish will chase each other out of their neighborhood. There are cleaning stations where fish are swimming up, and stopping, as cleaner fish forage all over them, cleaning off parasites. The politics of the reef I call it.

When we returned to the compound, we found there was to be a parade later that day. We made the best costumes we could. We used palm leaves, masks and snorkels, fins, and lots of duct tape. We rode on a flatbed truck squirting spectators with water guns. I think there were as many people in the parade, as there were spectators. That night there were multiple parties. We had taken a dozen cocos, and poured rum, and pineapple juice, in them; stuck a straw in them, and put them on ice. We decided to make the next day a day of no diving, so we knew we could hit the Pina Coladas pretty hard. I had one of the best times I ever had. There was a lot of laughing coming from Ned and Annie. It was kinda a Caribbean "Yah Mon" experience.

The next day we hung around the beach until we felt human again; then we explored some caves. It seems the pirates liked Caymans a lot, because there were lots of caves to hide their loot in. Also the slave traders hid the slaves there sometimes.

Scotty had to end his trip before us, and he left the next day, while we were diving. On our next dive we ran into lots of Nurse Sharks, and big Tarpans. Tarpans are usually very big and have scales the size of quarters. We were totally surrounded by a big school of them at one point. The Nurse sharks were very calm, and easy going as usual.

It came time to go to Cayman Brac on our way back to Grand Cayman. We said our "Goodbyes" to Annie, and the McCoy family, and were pretty sad to go.

When we got to Brac we needed a beer, so we went to a great looking outdoor bar. When we sat down, and ordered a "Red Stripe" the bartender asked "where were we from"? We told him Bennington. He said "Bennington - I've been to Bennington - that's the home of Benninglows". Bennington has more than its share of heavy, ugly women, so they started getting their own subspecies name - Benninglows! Kinda an off-shoot of Buffalo. It was hilarious to run into someone that knew about Bennington out in the middle of nowhere. We did a couple of dives on Brac, but they weren't quite as good as Little Cayman was. We did go out to my "sweet snorkeling spot", I had found on my first trip to Brac. It took forever to walk all the way out there, as Ned is one of the slowest walkers I've ever seen. But when we got out there, and swam from rock to rock with our stuff on our head, it was worth it. The visibility was fabulous, and the sharks, lobster, and fish were everywhere as usual. The sharks were curious, and actually nudged me with their nose probably looking for a "handout". We had only a couple of days on Brac, then we flew back to Grand Cayman. Joyce wasn't on Brac at the time. When we got to Grand Cayman we checked into a cheap, nondescript hotel room, and decided to set up a couple of scuba dives. We went on a boat with about a dozen divers aboard, and dove the bay out front. What a letdown. The coral was all beat up from too many divers; the visibility wasn't very good, and there was a boat full of Japanese divers in the same area. Japanese divers are notorious for diving in all directions, out of control. When Ned saw this he gave me the masterbaiting sign which means "cluster f--- diving". I had to agree.

We wanted to do something "cool" while we were on Grand Cayman, so we went over to "Stingray Bay". As usual we went out in the boat, waited until the Stingrays showed up, then fed them. This trip we spent a lot of time snorkeling the nearby reef, except this time there was a long line of Fusiliers and Batfish coming through constantly. There were also Eagle Rays and lots of really colorful Wrass. Wrass can come in as small as one inch to Napoleon Wrass that can be one hundred kilos. We got scooters, and went to some of my sweet snorkeling spots, and sent postcards from "Hell" again.

We finally had to leave Caymans, and we both agreed we had some great adventures. On the way back we got stuck on the tarmac in Houston for about two hours. The captain came on the intercom a couple of times, and claimed the strong winds were holding us there. We could see no wind out the window of the plane and thought it kinda odd.

When we returned Ned was talking about getting a boat worthy of diving out of. The first boat was a ski boat, and being a water skier since I was a kid, I enjoyed the couple of times we used it skiing. It was not a good dive boat. It was completely upholstered, and Ned was always worried about us ripping the upholstery.

He sold that one, and bought another one that was more suited to diving. We took it up to the Juans with his brother-in-law John. John was very smart, and a good diver, I really enjoyed. Since it was a cabin boat we could sleep on it. Much better than the first time Ned and I went up. We had to sleep on a little island called "Posey". It was a good island to sleep on, but it was no longer available because the state turned it into a "Kayak only" island. That night on Posey there was a "shooting star show" we watched. A couple of deer were on the island when we got there, but at nightfall they swam over to the next island. On the way out the next morning we hit a rock. We had to get a guy, on a big raft in Friday Harbor, to peen the prop out. We "limped" back home from there.

Ned's new boat besides, having a place to sleep, also had a galley. We kept crab pots out all the time. Besides crab we harvested a variety of fish, oysters, abalone, and scallops while diving. We ate "killer" meals, and had a freezer aboard, so we took fish and crab home as well.

One of our dives called John's Island was a collection of big boulders underwater. It was fun to swim through the openings between them, and I could always spot big ling cods laying under them. We had to carry a bar to pry abalone off the rock.

Another place called Spiden Bluff was a steep hill that went down hundreds of feet and always had lingcod, and the biggest Greenling I have ever seen. Both of these fish are excellent eating.

We anchored at Roach Harbor on Lopez Island. The boat that went around to collect the sewage from the boats is called the "Fecal Ferry". They claim "they'll take crap off of anyone". Haw haw! When the sun goes down they play taps in the harbor. It is quite a happening, as there is a lot of history there, since once most of the lye for concrete came from there. The old lye industry buildings, machinery, etc. are still there.

Back home that winter I was starting to snow ski with Ned, John and some others. We went to Salt Lake City Utah on a ski trip with a couple of other guys, Ned was acquainted with. We got an under one hundred dollar round trip from Seattle to Salt Lake City. Then we rented a room with a kitchenette from the Mormons. We also rented a four wheel drive Chevy and went to "Park City" the first day. At "Park City" you can take the ski lift from the street right down town.

Then we went to "Deer Park" and skied all day. We were impressed by the powdery snow. Each night we returned to our flat, and since we brought a whole cooler full of seafood, we had great meals. In the evening we went down to the pool right down the street, to get the kinks out.

The third day we went to "Solitude"; the best place so far. This place had good woods skiing and jumps. Since it was during the week it wasn't crowded.

The fourth day we went to "Snowbird". Each day the spots seemed to get better, and when we arrived here, there was a lot of wind, and snow; and we all loved it. When we got off the hill that day we all had snow clumped on our mustaches and hair.

The last day we went to Alta, only twenty five dollars then. I think this was the biggest of the places we visited. It was sunny and really easy going that day. I was skiing but we heard they don't allow snowboards here.

When all was said and done, we were all glad we went. The snow in Utah is drier than it is in Washington. But this would be the last time I would ski!

My boys were getting into snowboarding, and I had to give it a try. My boys, wife, and anyone of their friends that wanted to come, and I, went up to one of the passes on the weekend. I started using their boards, and after a couple of times all I wanted to do was snowboard. It was easy for me, as it's a lot like windsurfing. Soon my boys, and I were carving the woods, and chutes, and doing big jumps. We eventually got John to switch to snowboarding, but not Ned. The next spring, Ned and I wanted to go somewhere, so we decided to go to Costa Rica.

Cold but sweet!

COSTA RICA

Costa Rica wasn't really a great dive destination, but we didn't realize that until we got there. We flew to San Jose, and immediately got a rental car, and left there to go to Coco Beach, on the northern west coast.

The visibility was not good here at all. We arranged to do a three dive day trip out at the Cats and Bats, off the coast a ways. Ned saw a huge Whale shark that went right over my head, and I didn't see it. We saw some Bull sharks from a distance, and were happy to have some distance between us, and them. They can be dangerous!

I got a big Sailfish on my can line, while fishing off the dive boat. My can line only had ten kilo test line on it. There was no chance of getting this twenty five kilo fish into the boat. When my line broke, it had so much force, it put a red welt all the way up my arm. I got to play the big fish for a while before it broke off. What a rush!

Stingrays were doing triple back flips in the boat wake. We asked the skipper about it, and he said "that was common". I'd never seen that anywhere else.

I knew there was supposed to be good windsurfing up at Lake Aerinol, so we headed there. When we got there, there was no wind - wrong time of year. We drove around the lake, and headed south. When we got to La Fortuna we checked into a nice little bungalow at the base of Mount Aerinol. We knew Aerinol had been erupting, so we asked "where the mountain was". The landlord said "it was right in front of us", but we couldn't see it because it was all clouded in. He said "not to worry as it will clear off soon". He wasn't wrong. A couple hours later it cleared off; the ground started rumbling, and red hot rocks started flying out of the top. What a show, and we sat on our veranda sipping a beer, and watched the whole thing. We invited the two young ladies next door to come over and watch the show with us and they did.

The next day we went back north to watch the show from a different side of the mountain. We checked in at a park, and stayed until the next morning. The "show" had been equally good here.

The next morning we went south again to the Upper Suarales River. We heard we could river raft there. After arranging the trip, we rode with the guide, and a couple of other guests to our embarking point. As we arrived we saw a long bright green snake on the floor boards. The ladies screamed, and everyone piled out quickly. We noticed the guide was smiling. I don't think the snake was poisonous, and he put it there for a laugh.

The rafting went well after a "crash course" by the guide. There were Toucans, the colorful birds with the big beaks, in the trees. We were going right through the dense jungle. It took almost a half day, and the guide gave us all "Attaboys" for doing well in rough conditions. He took us back to our car, and we went on to Lemone on the Caribbean coast. We found out about the legendary bad potholes of Costa Rica first hand. We hit one on the highway so hard, we were surprised the windows didn't break in the car!

What a dump Lemone is. As we were slowly driving through with the windows down, we could hear people saying F-------- Americans. We could tell we weren't wanted there, and immediately headed south toward Panama. We stopped at an out of the way park, and went snorkeling. It wasn't very good there, as the visibility was bad, and the fish life poor. We left, and headed down to Puerto Viejo which means "old port". As we were pulling in, we noticed guys with guns patrolling the streets near the buildings. We stopped at a hotel, and found we were in a risky town, because it was on a drug trail. A relocated American guy sold us a little bit of "dew", and told us that an American girl was in the wrong place, at the wrong time, and was murdered recently along the trail. We buried the dew, and checked into a fairly good looking place in a small jungle. That night we woke up to a crook with a stiletto trying to cut a screen open, to get to Ned's wallet. Ned yelled at him, the local dogs started barking, and he ran off. The next day we arranged to go diving with a guide named Marco. He seemed to be O.K. but the dive stunk! There didn't seem to be anything alive including the reef. Marco said "the run off from all those banana plantations had killed the reef". We said "good riddance", and left the Caribbean coast, and headed over the mountains to the west coast. The whole trip over the mountains was all coffee plantations. It was kind of nice but boring.

Jaco Beach is known for its' good surf. I always loved to surf anywhere I could, so we headed to Jaco. We pulled into a nice looking place with Cabannas right on the beach. The young guy that managed the place, told us he wasn't quite open yet, but that he would give us a good deal on the place. We were the only ones there, and he let us use the big kitchen - what a deal!

We rented a couple of boards locally, and all I had to do was grab my board, and head down to our beach to surf. The break wasn't real good, but it was all right, and I had it to myself. Ned could never quite get surfing. The compound had a mote we had to cross to get in, and it had these lizards in it that ran across the water. I'd seen bullfrogs at home do it, but not lizards. This place was completely different from the all teak, second story place we stayed in at Coco Beach.

I got my fill of surfing, and we headed out to San Jose again. Somehow we got caught up in a road race, so we made the best of it. We stopped, and duct taped beer cans all over our car, and while we were in the race I yelled "Race Caro" to the crowds along the road. They responded by cheering us on. Of course we were very slow, and not really in the race, but it was fun anyway.

About all there was to do in San Jose before we flew out was shopping. They had a great outdoor market there. We came back by way of Mexico City, and after seeing it on our layover, we made up our minds to never go there again.

SEATTLE GRUNGE

Seattle was in the midst of the Grunge era. Any band that could play was being signed. My favorite band during this time was Alice in Chains, but I also liked Pearl Jam, Sound Garden, Nirvana, Queensryke, and Candlebox. There were also some bands like Janes Addiction, and Tool that weren't from Seattle, but were making good music.

I didn't think Primus and Blind Melon were making good music, even though they were both popular. I especially didn't like Blind Melon when I heard their lead singer urinated on the stage in Canada.

Fawn was really into Grunge, so Fawn, Frog, and I went to a concert in Portland featuring Pearl Jam. Neil Young and Blind Melon were also in the concert. When Pearl Jam came on; in the middle of a song, a guy jumped up on the stage. When the security guys started dragging him off the stage on his back, Eddie Vedder high fived the guy. We thought that showed a lot of class. Neil Young had a couple of guys from The Blues Brothers Band with him, but I really liked his acoustic set the most. His Strung out Junky song was the best. Neil Young suffers from Diabetes and Epilepsy both, and its' a wonder he can still perform so well.

The next time we went to a Grunge concert, was at the Gorge at George Washington - one of the prettiest concert venues on earth. That concert featured Alice in Chains and Primus. When Alice in Chains came on, after a couple of songs, Jerry Cantrell announced he had to take a break, to go "dump". He blamed it on an earlier burrito - first time I'd ever heard that! When he returned, they resumed with "Kill the Rooster", and the place erupted.

The next time we went to the Gorge was to hear Heart and Queensryke. A lot of great singing in this one with the great Wilson sisters of Heart, and Queensryke's good lead singer. Its' such a beautiful place with the Columbia River below, everyone sounds good there.

One of the concerts I missed there, that always haunted me was Stevie Ray Vaughn performing. He was so great but he

was killed in a helicopter wreck soon after. I think he did Jimi
Hendrix songs better than Jimi.

      The next Grunge concert was right in our own back yard
at the local fairground. My wife and I, and all the kids went to
this one. This was called Rockstock, and featured Soundgarden,
Tool, and Candlebox. Of course the music was outstanding, and
the weather co-operated as well.

      We always wished we could have seen Nirvana, but of
course when Curt "Cocaine" died, that wasn't going to happen.
Curt was from Aberdeen Washington on the coast, and to this
day the cities motto is "Come as you are"; famous words from
probably their greatest song. I still don't think Courtney Love
did much to keep her man alive!

      Seattle is a great music city, but like all good things,
Grunge has sort of faded away. It was exciting while it lasted.
A couple years later my wife and I went to a couple of good
concerts at the Gorge. The first was Led Zeppelin, or at least the
biggest part of Led Zeppelin; Page and Plant, along with a
backup band that even included violins. They sounded great,
and did most of their great songs. I couldn't help but notice a
little wimpy guy, kinda "weaseling" around, and we pronounced
him "the concert weasel". I think he was so "high" he had no
clue what he was doing. He skittered around just like a weasel.
The next concert Deener and I went to featured Bad Company,
Styx, and Billy Squire. Bad Company was the crowd favorite, as
when they ended, and Styx came on; the crowd started to leave.
I had seen Bad Company and Billy Squire before, so was
pumped to see Styx as well. The way they talked, they sounded
like they were in love with themselves, but when they started

playing they sounded perfect. They had a lot of good songs to play, but I liked "Miss America" the best.

For some reason when we started back home, I was thinking of a Johnny Carson's show where Arnold Palmer's wife was talking with Johnny. He asked her "if she did anything before a match to improve Arnold's game". She replied "she would kiss his balls". Johnny looked at the camera in his patented way, and said "I'll bet that made his putter sputter". What a classic moment.

Once we got home I started thinking about another dive trip. I was leaning toward a visit to the Red Sea in Egypt. I called Ned and he told me "I'm in" He was a commercial salmon fisherman at the time, and April is just before the season begins, so he was available.

CHAPTER 29

THE RED SEA

We both booked a free round trip to Egypt, as we had enough airline miles. We had to fly to New York, then to Amsterdam, where we had an all-day layover.

The first stop in Amsterdam was the museum that featured Rembrandt paintings, with Picasso, and other paintings also. On our way in we walked by a guy and "chick" sitting on a bench out front "shooting up". Other than that it was a great experience to see all those famous paintings including "Whistlers Mother".

When we left there we went to a big local park, full of young people smoking, drinking, shooting up, and other dastardly deeds. It was early afternoon so we hung for a while then headed down town.

Amsterdam is full of canals, lined with medium sized buildings. Some of the building fronts are shored up by poles run diagonally to the concrete on the edge of the canal, so they wouldn't fall over.

Pot was legal so we went to a coffee house for food, tea for me, and a "joint" afterward. After our meal when we got to the joint; I lit it and took a drag. I almost "hacked my guts out". The pot was mixed with tobacco, and we didn't know it was. We couldn't handle it, so we set out to find some pot that wasn't mixed with tobacco.

We came to a storefront that read "Marijuana Museum" on the door. I could see a big plant standing toward the back.

The store was full of pot paraphernalia, along with pot, hash, keif, etc. We eventually got to a displaced American, who had a big clear glass vessel that had a bowl attached as well as a neck to draw smoke from. He asked if "we wanted a toke", we said "sure" and took a couple of hits. I asked him what it was, and he said "Green Bud". I said well "Green Bud is good, but we really liked Hash". He started patting multiple pockets on his coat, and said "I have some right here"! After he loaded the bowl, we started taking hits. Then I said "Hash is good, but we also liked Keif". He loaded the bowl with Keif. After a while we could hardly stand, and we headed out for the "Red Light district". These were alleys full of naked women dancing in their cubicles, in front of glass doors. Of course we were both married, and not going for it, but it was a strange sight anyway. I thought I could see the wheels turning in Ned's head.

We finally started stumbling back toward the transportation station. We asked a cop on the corner where the station was, he gave us directions, then smiled and asked "if we thought we could get there"! We found it, then set out on a light rail to the airport.

Our next stop was Sharm el Sheikh, Sinai, Egypt. It was on the southern coast of the Sinai Peninsula, on the upper end of the Red Sea. The peninsula separates the Gulf of Suez, and the Gulf of Aqaba.

We came in late at night, and checked into a cluster of little huts, called the "Pigeon Hole". We were tired, and had no problem "crashing".

The next day we set up our diving, and the first was in the Straits of Tiran. It was good diving. We saw lots of Spanish

Dancers, Crocodile Fish, Stone fish, Unicorn Fish, various
Wrasses, and Cleaner Fish. Unicorn Fish are distinctive because
they have a long thorn on their forehead.

That night we went across the road, to a big hotel on the
water, to night snorkel with lights. Critters are out at night that
are not out during the day. There were lots of Spanish Dancers,
Crocodile Fish, Groupers, and Slipper Lobsters.

The next day we were to go on a wreck dive called the
"Thistlegorm". Seems it was a WWII English freighter that had
been spotted by a German bomber. The plane dropped a bomb
down the smokestack. It had a locomotive and a couple of
freight cars on tracks on the main deck. Inside it had other war
supplies, along with a couple hundred men. When the ship went
down in about thirty meters, the train fell off to the side, and the
ship settled upright on the bottom. When we first left our boat to
swim over to the "Thistlegorm", we could see lots of bubbles
escaping the hull from divers that were already inside the hull.
We first inspected the train next to the hull. It was an odd sight -
that train on the bottom. When we went inside the hull we were
among hundreds of motorcycles, standing intact, that had a light
layer of sediment on them that resembled dust. Then we came to
lines of helmets, dishes, submarine periscopes, guns, everything
war. It was very impressive, because everything was in such
good shape. We went to a couple of other dives in the area on
various reefs, but the wreck was the highlight.

That night we walked over to the big hotel complex,
after a great dinner of Pita bread, and roasted chicken we scored
on the street. There just happened to be entertainment. Though
a lot of it was in a foreign tongue, we enjoyed the singing, and
dancing. A lot of it was designed to incorporate the crowd, and

we had a lot of fun with it. It was challenging to sing in a foreign tongue.

The next day we went out to a spot on Tiran, and another in the Gulf of Aqaba. There was an Italian guy with us that was always "whining" about "wanting to see a shark". I cut a shark picture out of a magazine, and put it in his mask, so when he put it on, Ned said "now you see the shark"! Everyone got a good laugh out of that one! The next day this same guy "busted" his head open, trying to jump from our boat to another, and with the stitches his diving was over.

The next night we would say "Goodbye" to Sharm, and head up in the Gulf of Aqaba by bus, to a place called Dahab. It took quite a few hours, and it seemed the bus had dropped us off in the middle of nowhere. We were told to "walk down the hill toward Aqaba to the little town. When I stepped around the corner onto the "main drag", I'll never forget that first look at Dahab. It was all lit up like Las Vegas on a smaller scale. Across the street from the line of storefront businesses, was a carved out area lined in carpets, right on the sea. There was a big "Hooka" in the middle of the covered digs, with Bedouins smoking out of it. Next to this was about fifty camels, they rode in on. I could see this place was a melting pot of peoples, something like Paia, Hawaii. We rented a nice little open, stucco, and tile room for cheap, in a place called "The Camel Lot".

The next morning we set up our dives. Our Dive master was a "Brit" named Ian. We liked him instantly, and went out on a couple of dives on a reef out front. The first dive had a great field of Garden eels. These eels were up to a meter tall and were spaced about every three inches. They suck down into their holes when they see someone. The trick to getting right in among them, is to creep in as slow as possible, laying right on the bottom. Since they live in sand, I was slowing down my breathing so I made less bubbles. It's quite a thrill to be in among them, as they sway back and forth with the current. Also the Stone Fish and Crocodile Fish, were more numerous than we had ever witnessed before. The two were in a reef that started up along the side of the Garden eel bed, and continued at a slope up to about a meter deep, coming from twenty meters deep. Ned and I were really getting it all very good, because we were the only two divers he was guiding - what service!

That night Ned and I got a fish from the local market, and cooked it with some rice in an adjoining community kitchen. The locals seemed surprised that we knew enough to look at the gills, to see if it's fresh. Ned and I were both fisherman, so we should know how to check for freshness.

The first dive the next day, was at a place called "The Blue Hole". We walked out on the one meter deep flat reef, to a blue hole in the turquoise. It was about two meters wide, and went straight down. We jumped in, and followed the tube to about twenty meters deep. Then it went sideways about ten meters over to a big blue room. First we entered another smaller room about three or four meters high. This room was full of Glass fish, which shine when they move, usually in unison. We kinda sat along the side watching them, then Ian took his regulator out of his mouth, and opened wide. A cleaner fish came up from behind him, went in his mouth, and started cleaning his teeth. I thought I was going to drown from laughing in my regulator. After we got over this one, we went into the

Blue Hole that was about twenty meters wide and had a big hole in one wall that was open to Aqaba. It was all quite majestic. We were joined on the next dive by an Israeli lawyer, an Egyptian guy, and an Arabic couple. We dove the other end of the good reef that had Garden eel, Crocodile, and Stone fish. This time it also had a fifty kilo Grouper as well as the other species. We also spotted a couple of different eels that we had never seen before.

That night we all had a Stella Beer around the table, and "bullshitted" for hours. The Israeli lawyer told a lot of jokes. It really struck me, an Israeli, and Egyptian having a beer together, when they are made out to be enemies. It kinda made me wonder about government's truthfulness.

Ian told us a while back, there was a camel race at a local fair. One of the Bedouins started whipping his camel, because he wouldn't move. Some American guy yelled at him to "stop beating the camel", and he didn't. The "yank" went over, and grabbed the Bedouin, and punched him out, to the pleasure of the crowd. It made a good story, and if it is true, then I'm proud to be a "yank"!

Our next dive day was truly wild. The Bedouins provided us with camels to ride. They loaded all our dive gear, and other stuff on some other camels. Camels were not bad to ride. They resembled riding a horse with a lot of forward sway. It was kind of a rhythm thing. We rode about fifteen kilometers south, and staged up on a flat spot right next to the beach. The first dive was between big boulders. Some turtles, and assorted

A face only a mother could love

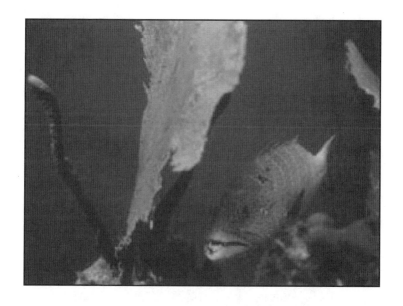

Hey you talking to me?

Spines Anyone?

fish were around. The same crew was along today as yesterday, except the Egyptian was absent.

The Bedouins had a white tent set up for us, and served us tea, while we laid around. A diver has to spend about two hours on the surface between dives degassing.

The next two dives were also nearby, but the bottom was different. Some of it was Garden eel bed, while some of it was eel grass. There were small balmies around that had Glass fish and other Neons hanging around the eroded bottoms. During my surface time, I used my can line, casting to get a little fish to catch a big fish. I never caught the big fish, but is was so "cool" standing up to my waist in the water at one meter on top of the reef, just before it dropped off deep watching fish through the clear water.

We finished up our diving and rode our "steeds" back. It had been a big adventure, but we set our sights on the next! The next evening we took a cab to the Monastery, then walked all the way to the top of Mount Sinai. When we walked up towards the Monastery, a bunch of Egyptian cab drivers were walking with us. One, a smart ass, started giving me "crap", because I had my Bedouin head gear on. The Bedouins had given me the gear as it is the best way to keep from getting burned up. It has a flap when tied right that can be placed on whatever side of my head I want to keep out of the sun. I can pour water on the top, and it slowly runs down, and keeps my head cool. Anyway the "wise guy" was acting like, because I am American - I cannot wear Bedouin head gear - absurd! I happened to notice he was wearing Levi's, and said "Levi's are American - you shouldn't wear them unless you're American".

Everybody there laughed, and the "dumb ass" shut up! It was a
long, long walk up to the top; about five hours. The last part is
the infamous "ten thousand steps". The sunrise is supposed to be
the big thing to see, so we rented a thick blanket from the
Bedouins, and camped out on a flat spot. I didn't think the
sunrise was at all good. It was all smogged in so we headed back
down. We tried to burn a bush in Moses's honor, but couldn't
find a bush; just trash. When we got back down we got our ride
back with a different cabby. The other guy was driving with his
headlights off, in the moonlight; at least this guy didn't seem as
wild, and drove a bit more reassuring.

We'd pretty much dove all the best spots in the area, so
we set out on the bus for Sharm. This time we stopped just long
enough to get our pita bread, and a roast chicken then we
boarded the ferry for Hurghada on the main land. The ferry was
a triple decker passenger only thirty meter vessel. It was sort of
rough looking, and moved slowly. I thought the boat was
moving about the right speed for fishing; so I got out my can
line, and set it up with a hand tied monofilament leader with a
plastic squid. No weight just a small swivel. A couple of hours
out I caught a Tuna. They stopped the ferry, and I fought my
fish from the fantail of the boat, and landed it while everyone
looked on. It was about a four kilo tuna. I started fishing again
while the ferry chugged on. About an hour later I got one on that
appeared to weigh nine or ten kilos. I was playing it, and the
boat was stopping, when a local guy grabbed my line, and started
trying to bring my fish in. By the time I got the guy to let go of
my line; the fish had broken off. I was pissed, but went easy on
him anyway.

The crew wanted my plastic squid, since they were fishing with their poles the whole time I was fishing, and had gotten "zilch"! I wouldn't give them my Hoochie but gave them the tuna. We were on the move and couldn't cook it anyway. Our ultimate destination wasn't Hurghada because while researching it we decided diving there would be boring so we headed down the Red Sea to a place called ElQuseir. This town had an old medieval castle in the middle of it which the U.S. was rebuilding. We found a place to stay that was affiliated with a dive operation. It was right next to the Red Sea, where it was kinda rough out front, and the beach wasn't very good. Sometimes, when we were desperate to get wet we swam out front anyway.

We got going on setting up our dives, and were surprised to find, it would be shore dives for seventeen bucks a dive. What a deal for these dives. The room had a tiny kitchen, but it did the job. I always cook my own meals if possible, because restaurants have poisoned me before. The next morning we met the dive master at about 8 a.m. He took us to a place that was very cool to swim around in. It had big jagged stones standing that were as big as buildings. It seemed like the canals were formed by all the big rocks. Depths varied down to forty meters. There were some fish here, but the real deal was swimming in these underwater canals. There were a lot of turtles in the water. There was also a big Moray eel swimming in and out of his hole.

During our surface time we hung in a Bedouin tent while they brought us tea. There were five divers total, so when the dive master found out we had thousands of dives between us, he said "we could guide ourselves if we wanted to". We declined,

and told him "we would stick with him". The dive masters dive
these places nearly every day and know them better than anyone.
They always know where the most desired things to see are
located.

That evening we wanted to go to town but we lived
about a mile away. Each night at about six p.m. the loudspeaker
from town went off with the daily Muslim prayer. It sounded
like a bunch of singing "gibberish" and could be annoying. Ned
proclaimed "get used to it, we'll be here a while". There was a
local VW bus we could ride to town, but we spotted a ten year
old kid with a donkey cart. We thought we would rather pay him
for a ride than pay the bus. When we got on his cart, there were
a couple of kids in the field there, and one of them "hit me up",
but we would not give anyone money, just peanuts and cookies.
When I gave the kid his, he yelled, and about fifty kids came
running, and cleaned me out. The kid with the cart was named
Iman, and when we pulled into town, shop owners were calling
him by name, and talking to him. It didn't seem like they were
saying anything derogatory about us, but just commenting about
Iman hauling "Gringo's to town".

We said "Bye" to Iman, and set out buying a fish for
dinner. I had a kilo weight from my dive belt on me, and when I
put it on the scale in a store, it showed the proprietor's scale read
a little heavy. The other patrons in the store started getting on
the proprietor, like they didn't appreciate his scales, and lack of
honesty.

A guy from South Africa we were diving with, had
showed me how to count in Arabic. I asked the proprietor in
another store what the price was of an item I wanted, and he told

me a high price. I said "no, it says right here the price is $2.50", and he looked astounded, and asked "you know how to count in Arabic" and I told him "yes"! It showed me the shop proprietors weren't exactly truthful, but it came in handy in our dealings.

We went to the medieval castle in the mid town, and were impressed by the view from there of the town, and region for miles around. We found out that the good "ole" U.S.A. was paying for the restoration of the fortress. We left for our room, to cook up the fish we had bought.

When we walked into the lobby, the guy behind the counter asked us "if we were going to cook the fish we bought in town. How did he know about the fish, when we had it in our pack, out of sight? I guess word passes quickly in small towns.

The next day's dives were also good, not a lot of fish, but each dive had different topography. We were at about forty five meters deep, alone, when Ned spotted a big Green turtle, and grabbed him by the back, and went for a ride. The big turtle didn't seem to mind too much, and Ned was all pumped up. Also on this dive we ran into an area like a cave full of Glass fish, with bigger fish swimming around amongst them. It was very eerie looking and the big fish looked like ghosts.

When we got finished diving that day, and returned to our hotel, we decided to get into our lock box, and get some money out. Ned said "he was missing a hundred dollar bill"! We both counted each other's money, and wrote it down when we put it in there. I checked it with what I had written down, and sure enough, he was right. We noticed the counter guy had moved off, and was trying his best to ignore us. He just shrugged us off, so we asked for the manager. When we talked to him, he just said "you are mistaken".

After we gave the kids peanuts and cookies at the field, we headed to town. We noticed a two story building with "Commissioner of Police" written on it. There were military looking Police coming, and going. We went upstairs to the commissioner's office, and told him through a translator, about the hundred dollars. He told us to sit down. Soon there were translators and about a half dozen individuals sitting in front of the commissioner's desk. We told our story in detail, and the commissioner told the translator to tell us "he was going to send for the manager". The Bedouins brought in tea, and we all sat around drinking tea, and talking, until the manager showed up. When the manager showed up, the commissioner grilled him for a while. We could see the commissioner's brow raise in disbelief, and wondered what had happened. Turned out the manager told him they didn't have a key to the lock boxes - an obvious lie - of course they have a key. Through the interpreter the commissioner informed us, we would be reimbursed the hundred by the manager. I told them "I broke a glass top on a table, and to deduct it". We ended up getting eighty three dollars back, but it was all like a scene out of "Casablanca"!

The next day we did our final dives there, which of course were good.

During our surface time, we were all sitting around drinking Bedouin tea in the tent when a cop rode up on a camel. Ned went out, and took a picture. Next thing I know, the cop is chasing Ned around the truck trying to take the film. He didn't appreciate Ned taking his picture, so Ned said "he had only taken a picture of the camel". The cop said "just camel" and Ned said

"Yes". That appeased the cop, and he backed off. I thought I was going to see Ned on "Cops in Egypt" or something! Back in the early nineties a bunch of tourists were killed by terrorists at Luxor, so the whole country was very security conscious. Tourism had decreased by about seventy five percent because of the tragedy at Luxor, and the country was still trying to recover from it. Anytime we took buses, the cops stopped the buses periodically to check each passenger's passport. They always apologized and we always told them "not to, as we appreciated them keeping us safe". Even when we went to a huge resort owned by Movenpick Ice Cream Company, we had to drive around a machine gun nest to get inside the gate. The next day we headed out for Cairo, the end of our journey to Egypt. While we were waiting for our bus in ElQuseir, a flatbed truck with short sides pulled up. It had about a dozen camels in it. It looked so funny, a dozen camel heads sticking up, because that was all of the camel we could see.

Our bus came, and we were off to Cairo. Cairo is a huge city that looks totally out of control. They drive like "madmen" there. I thought we would get in a few accidents on the trip, but surprisingly we got to an old hotel right down town unscathed. We checked in, and went right out to find our chicken, and pita dinner. The drivers there pay no attention to traffic lights, and we pretty much had to "run for it" a lot. We found our food and went down to a local park. I was already getting tired of getting hit up by street bums. This was the worst I had ever been hounded - it was even worse than Mexico.

The next day we got a cab out to the pyramids at Giza.

Of course the cab driver on his own, stopped at a gift shop, and tried to get us to buy stuff. I didn't want anything, but Ned bought a couple of trinkets.

We finally got to Giza, and went up to an upper deck of a hotel, that looked right down on the Sphinx. Cairo is built right up to the pyramids.

They always show desert around the pyramids, but in reality that is only on one side.

We got donkeys, and went through the chain length gate out in the pyramids. We were told that the Germans had blown the nose off the Sphinx during World War II, and wouldn't return it. Most of the pyramids were blocked off, and couldn't be accessed.

We finally went back to the big hotel overlooking the Sphinx, and got a couple of cold "Stellas". We sat, and just looked at the whole scene. We tried to relax, but were bombarded by people wanting something - mostly our money! We got so annoyed, we got a different cab, and got the hell out of there. We asked the driver to take us to the Nile River that runs through the middle of Cairo. We wanted to get on a boat just to get away from the "hounding bums". It worked, and for an hour or so we were not getting bothered on the boat. The Nile is a crusty river, like all that run through cities seem to be.

We found food and went back to our run down old hotel. The next day we were going to the museum.

The museum in Cairo, as far as I can see, is the best thing going in Cairo. It is based on all the old Egyptian stuff that was removed from the Pyramids. The first thing we saw when we went in was a huge stone lion laying on the first floor.

There's a lot of "cool" other stuff on the first floor but when we got to the next floor, which was a mezzanine I found Nefertiti laying in an open coffin, next to Ramseys in his open coffin - both of course are mummified. I was sad to hear that this museum was looted in later years!

The next day we flew out, with just a short stop in Amsterdam, and New York. We were on a plane sitting near a couple of guys from my home town.

When I got home I got ill with flu like symptoms. I called one of the guys from the plane, and found they were also ill with the same symptoms.

I eventually got over it, and set about fixing an old house I had purchased. I called it "polishing a turd"! A couple of months later there came one of the worst days of my life - 9/11. My kids woke me in the morning, and wanted me to turn on the TV. I could hardly believe what I was seeing - planes full of people crashing into our buildings. I wondered how much this act of terrorism would change our lives!

The End?

Bevis and Butthead do Egypt

Thank you so much for reading this book. I hope you enjoyed reading it as much as I enjoyed writing it.

Watch for the Further Adventures of Mr. Zig Zag as well as the Furthest Adventures of Mr. Zig Zag

Order this or any other Mr. ZigZag book at
www.zigzagbooksjck.com Or call John at (360) 830-4429

John Juan

Rear cover photo by Ted Manos

In Memory of Rico